INSTRUCTOR'S AND SOLUTIONS MANUAL WITH TESTS

RICHARD C. SPRINTHALL AND CAROL S. SPAFFORD

Second Edition

BASIC STATISTICAL ANALYSIS

Richard C. Sprinthall

American International College

PRENTICE-HALL, INC.
Englewood Cliffs, New Jersey 07632

© 1987 by **PRENTICE-HALL, INC.**
A Division of Simon & Schuster
Englewood Cliffs, N.J. 07632

ISBN: 0-13-067711-6

Printed in the United States of America

CONTENTS

ANSWERS TO EVEN NUMBERED TEXT PROBLEMS

INTRODUCTION

This instructor's manual has been prepared to accompany Sprinthall's Basic Statistical Analysis and was written by Richard C. Sprinthall and Carol S. Spafford. The purpose of this manual is to aid the busy instructor. Large student enrollments, students with varying educational backgrounds, and a course which students often approach with trepidation . . . all combine to present the instructor in elementary statistics with a most difficult job.

There is probably no other college course which is more demanding of the instructor's time than elementary statistics. The majority of students look forward to the course with the same enthusiasm they'd have for being the victims at a public flogging. These students need time and attention, office-hour visits, extra sessions, and perhaps most of all, lots of problems to work out and immediate feedback. This all takes time, and in many cases, the instructor who has perhaps three other courses to prepare, simply doesn't have enough of that precious commodity--time.

Feedback and constant practice are the essential ingredients for student success in elementary statistics. The student who puts things off, and "lets it get away," may find it impossible to catch up. Unlike a history course, where the student can spend an entire weekend doing catch-up reading, the student in elementary statistics needs daily involvement. And daily student involvement translates into more work for the instructor--making up problems, doing the problems, and correcting the problems.

Hopefully, this manual will help ease the instructor's burden. There are a total of over 1600 test items in this manual. There are approximately 900 Multiple-Choice items, 400 True-False items, and 350 problems requiring calculated solutions. Except for Chapters 1 and 11, which do not demand any calculations, each chapter has a large number of problems where actual values have been worked out. These may be used as homework problems, or as exam items. Further, both the Multiple-Choice and the True-False items are odd-even balanced throughout each chapter. If the even-numbered items are used for the main exam, the odd-numbered items may be used for the students needing a make-up exam. The items are designed to be straight-forward and unambiguous. They are not intended to trick the student, but instead to provide an honest evaluation of the student's ability. There are no "curve balls" or "sliders": instead, the questions all come "right-down-the-middle," and although some may require a careful reading, the student who is thoughtful and prepared should not find them difficult.

Finally, the manual also includes the answers to all even-numbered text problems (The odd-numbered answers are presented in the text itself).

For all problems requiring mathematical calculations, the rounding method used in the book is to round each calculation to two digits to the right of the decimal point (the hundredths place). The convention has been adopted of rounding up one digit when the rounded number is a "5". This is consistent with the method built into the hand calculators (on those models which can be set automatically to round off). Although there may well be some minor discrepancies between your answers and those to follow, these will most probably be due to rounding differences and, therefore, should be small.

A. Multiple Choice Items

1. The inherent fallacy in the argument that capital punishment is not a
   deterrent (since pockets were being picked even at the public hanging
   of a pickpocket) is that

   a. pickpockets were never hanged
   b. you can't compare groups of unequal sizes
   *c. there was no comparison or control group
   d. you can't make comparisons with only nominal data

2. Whenever two events occur simultaneously, such as increasing numbers of
   joint bank accounts and increasing numbers of felonies, one must be
   careful not to

   *a. assume that one event is the cause of the other
   b. assume that any correlation exists between them
   c. assume that the data have been reported honestly
   d. all of these

3. The founding of probability theory is popularly credited to

   a. the Chevalier de Mere
   b. Sir Francis Galton
   c. Karl Pearson
   *d. Blaise Pascal

4. William Sealy Gossett, the statistician at the Guinness Brewing Company,
   published his works using the pen name

   a. Professor
   b. Blaise Pascal
   c. Cicero
   *d. Student

5. Statistics as a general field is divided into two sub-areas. They are

   a. predictive and inferential
   *b. descriptive and inferential
   c. nominal and ordinal
   d. none of these

6. When we say that the average height of all adult females in the U.S. is
   5'4", we are using

   a. nominal data
   b. ordinal data
   c. inferential statistics
   *d. descriptive statistics

7. Techniques which are used for describing large amounts of data in
   abbreviated form, are called

   *a. descriptive statistics   b. inferential statistics
   c. predictive statistics   d. probability estimates

8. The difference between inferential and predictive statistics is that

    a. inferential extrapolates, whereas predictive does not
    b. predictive extrapolates, whereas inferential does not
    c. inferential assumes that a sample has been measured, whereas predictive makes no such assumption
 *d. there is no difference between them

9. When a researcher attempts to estimate the characteristics of an entire population, the techniques employed are called

 *a. inferential statistics
    b. descriptive statistics
    c. skewed statistics
    d. b and c, but not a

10. The researcher using inferential statistics always makes predictions which are based on having measured

    a. population
 *b. a sample
    c. the entire group being predicted
    d. in inferential statistics predictions are never made

11. The goal of the researcher using inferential statistics is to

    a. make better-than-chance predictions
    b. predict the characteristics of the entire group, based on measures taken on a smaller group
    c. describe the difference between the highest and lowest score
 *d. a and b, but not c

12. An example of a variable would be

    a. height
    b. weight
    c. the number of inches in a foot
 *d. a and b, but not c

13. Anything which can be measured and observed to vary is called

    a. a constant
 *b. a variable
    c. an integer
    d. all of these

14. The assigning of numbers to measurements according to certain rules is called

    a. prediction
    b. point estimation
    c. matrix formation
 *d. measurement

15. When numbers are assigned on the basis of discrete, mutually exclusive categories, the resulting scale is called

 *a. nominal   b. ordinal
    c. interval   d. ratio

16. When data are in nominal form, the only information provided is

    *a. the frequency of occurrence within categories
     b. greater than or less than, but not how much greater or less
     c. the value of absolute zero
     d. nominal data provide no information

17. When the measurement scale provides information regarding greater than or less than, but not how much greater or less, it is in the form of

     a. nominal data
    *b. ordinal data
     c. interval data
     d. ratio data

18. An example of a nominal scale would be

    *a. the number of pieces of mail going to Post Office A versus Post Office B
     b. the recorded heights of a group of first-grade children
     c. the order of finish for the horses at the Kentucky Derby
     d. all of these

19. Whenever we discover how many persons, things, or events have X or Y in common, we are dealing with the

    *a. nominal scale
     b. ordinal scale
     c. interval scale
     d. the mere number of persons, things, or events having X or Y in common cannot be scaled

20. Whenever measured observations are rank ordered, the data form is

     a. nominal
    *b. ordinal
     c. interval
     d. rank-ordered observations cannot be measured

21. When the only mathematical rule involved is that of equality versus non-equality, the measurement scale must be

    *a. nominal
     b. ordinal
     c. interval
     d. ratio

22. Whenever we are given information regarding both equality versus non-equality and greater than or less than, the data form is

     a. nominal
    *b. ordinal
     c. interval
     d. the concept of "greater than" cannot be scaled

3

23. Whenever we are presented with "nose-counting" data, such as how many persons are registered as republicans versus those registered as democrats, the data form is

   *a. nominal
    b. ordinal
    c. interval
    d. ratio

24. If school children are categorized on the basis of whether or not they exhibit overt aggression during a free-play period, the data form is

   *a. nominal
    b. ordinal
    c. interval
    d. data which are merely categorized fit no specific scale type

25. When measures provide information of not just greater than or less than, but also how much greater or less, the data form is

    a. nominal
    b. ordinal
   *c. interval
    d. a and b, but not c

26. When frequency data are categorized into a nominal scale, the categories must

    a. overlap slightly
    b. overlap completely
   *c. be completely independent
    d. frequency data cannot form a nominal scale

27. The concept of "mutually exclusive" categories is central to

   *a. nominal scaling
    b. ordinal scaling
    c. interval scaling
    d. both a and c, but not b

28. If we were to know not only the order of finish of the cars at the Indianapolis "500", but also the actual elapsed times for each car, the data form would be

    a. at least nominal
    b. at least ordinal
   *c. at least interval
    d. none of these

29. If the population of registered voters in a given district were to be rank-ordered on the basis of socio-economic status, the data form would be

    a. at least nominal
   *b. at least ordinal
    c. at least interval
    d. socio-economic status cannot be measured

30. The difference between interval and ratio scales is that ratio scales

   a. form independent categories
   b. form ordered sequences
   *c. have absolute zeroes
   d. there is no difference

31. Most social scientists treat IQ data as though they are

   a. nominal
   b. ordinal
   *c. interval
   d. ratio

32. Whenever the distances between successive scale points are assumed to be equal, the scale of measurement is at least

   a. nominal
   b. ordinal
   *c. interval
   d. ratio

33. With interval data, we can say everything <u>except</u>

   a. X differs from Y
   b. X is greater than Y
   c. X is two units greater than Y
   *d. X is twice Y

34. The reason that it is incorrect to say that person A's IQ is twice person B's is that IQ is <u>not</u> scaled as

   a. nominal data
   b. ordinal data
   c. interval data
   *d. ratio data

35. Of all the measurement scales covered in this chapter, the one containing the most information is the

   a. nominal scale
   b. ordinal scale
   c. interval scale
   *d. ratio scale

36. Of all the measurement scales covered in this chapter, the one containing the least information is the

   *a. nominal scale
   b. ordinal scale
   c. interval scale
   d. ratio scale

37. The issue of which scale of measurement has been used largely determines

   *a. which statistical tests can be used
   b. whether the statistics are descriptive or inferential
   c. whether the statistics are inferential or predictive
   d. whether the data have been "rigged" or "faked"

5

38. The concept of generalizing from a few observations to an entire group is central to the area of

    a. descriptive statistics
    b. nominal scaling
    c. ratio scaling
  * d. inferential statistics

39. Of the following, the measures which comes closest to ratio scaling are

    a. the numbers of people using flouride versus non-flouride toothpaste
    b. the final standings of the American League East's baseball teams
    c. the area codes used for direct telephone dialing
  * d. the salaries of a group of factory workers

40. If it is known that X is greater than Y, and that is all that is known, then the measurement scale must be

    a. nominal
  * b. ordinal
    c. interval
    d. a descriptive measure of this type can never be scaled

41. The measured heights of a group of basketball players form a(n)

    a. nominal scale
    b. ordinal scale
    c. interval scale
  * d. ratio scale

42. Statistical tests designed to handle interval data, may also be used on

    a. nominal data
    b. ordinal data
  * c. ratio data
    d. a test designed for interval data cannot handle data of any other type

43. Nominal data can always be converted into

    a. ordinal data
    b. interval data
    c. ratio data
  * d. nominal data cannot be converted into any other scale since it depends only on equality versus non-equality

44. The statement that one can prove anything with statistics is only true when

    a. the data have been faked
  *b. the reader is naive regarding statistical procedures
    c. the statement is always true
    d. the statement is never true

6

45. The first attempt to employ statistical techniques for estimating population parameters was designed in order to

    *a. estimate beer-drinking tastes in Dublin, Ireland
    b. calculate the odds for casino gambling in France
    c. calculate the probability of certain exponential functions
    d. all of these

46. The first attempt to employ probability theory in a practical setting was developed in order to

    a. predict the results of presidential elections
    b. predict economic forces in the market place
    c. predict how consumers will evaluate new products
    *d. make winning bets in the gambling casinos

B. True or False: For the following, indicate T (true) or F (false)

47. Descriptive statistics are designed to infer population values.   F

48. Descriptive statistics provide symbolic techniques for describing large groups of data.   T

49. Inferential statistics involve the measuring of a sample and then using this value for predicting to the population.   T

50. Inferential statistical techniques and predictive statistical techniques are identical.   T

51. The frequency of occurrence within mutually exclusive categories provides nominal data.   T

52. The concept of "greater than or less than" is a crucial component of nominal data.   F

53. With interval data, there must be an absolute zero point.   F

54. Ordinal data provide information regarding greater than or less than, but not how much greater or less.   T

55. Interval data require that there be an equal distance between successive scale points.   T

56. The mathematical rule of "equality versus non-equality" is central to nominal data.   T

57. Nominal data always imply equal distances between successive scale points.   F

58. With ordinal data, assumptions can be made regarding how much greater X is than Y.   F

59. Since IQ data are interval, then one can safely say that an IQ of 140 is twice as high as an IQ of 70.   F

60. Measurement is the assigning of numbers to observations according to certain rule.   T

61. Statements such as "twice as large" or "half as large" can only be made when the data are ordinal   F

CHAPTER 2
GRAPHS AND MEASURES OF CENTRAL TENDENCY

A. Multiple Choice Items

1. When scores are arranged in order of magnitude, the researcher has formed a

   a. histogram
   b. measure of centrality
   c. measure of dispersion
   *d. distribution

2. Traditionally, the researcher indicates frequency of occurrence on the graph's

   *a. ordinate
   b. abscissa
   c. line of ascent
   d. horizontal axis

3. When single points are used to designate the frequency of each score, the points being connected by a series of straight lines, this is called a

   *a. frequency polygon
   b. frequency rectangle
   c. scatter plot
   d. histogram

4. The mean, median, and mode are all measures of

   a. dispersion
   b. variability
   *c. central tendency
   d. all of these

5. When a graph is constructed using a series of rectangles indicating the frequency of occurrence for each score, it is called a

   a. frequency polygon
   b. frequency rectangle
   c. scatter plot
   *d. histogram

6. The measurement which occurs most often in a distribution is called the

   a. median
   b. percentile
   c. mean
   *d. mode

7. When a distribution is skewed, the researcher should use the

   a. mean
   *b. median
   c. mode
   d. all of these are appropriate

8. When a distribution shows a large majority of very low scores and a few
    very high scores, the distribution is said to be

    *a. skewed to the right
    b.   skewed to the left
    c.   skewed to the middle
    d.   bimodal

9. The influence of a few extreme scores in one direction is most pro-
    nounced on the value of the

    *a. mean
    b.   median
    c.   mode
    d.   percentile

10. Using the mean to indicate centrality on a distribution of income
    scores usually results in

    a.   a false image of poverty
    b.   an accurate portrayal of income
    *c. a false image of prosperity
    d.   income scores never lend themselves to centrality

11. When each score is listed in order of magnitude, together with the
    number of individuals receiving each score, the researcher has set up

    a.   a unimodal distribution
    b.   a bimodal distribution
    c.   a skewed distribution
    *d. a frequency distribution

12. The abscissa is

    *a. the horizontal axis
    b.   the vertical axis
    c.   the connected points on a polygon
    d.   a measure of central tendency

13. On a frequency distribution, raw scores are plotted on the

    *a. abscissa
    b.   ordinate
    c.   vertical axis
    d.   all of these, depending on the size of the group being measured

14. When graphing data, it is traditional to make the length of the ordinate
    equal to

    a.   the length of the abscissa
    b.   twice the length of the abscissa
    *c. three-quarters of the length of the abscissa
    d.   one-half of the length of the abscissa

15. The difference between the histogram and the bar graph is that the
    histogram

    a.   indicates frequency, whereas the bar graph doesn't

b. indicates the measured scores, whereas the bar graph doesn't
c. indicates centrality, whereas the bar graph doesn't
*d. there is no difference between them

16. With a frequency polygon, scores are always presented on

*a. the X axis
b. the Y axis
c. the Z axis
d. the frequency polygon may never be used to represent scores

17. The ordinate is identical to the

a. X axis
*b. Y axis
c. mean
d. none of these

18. The so-called "wow" graph is always possible whenever

a. scores are presented on the X axis
b. the abscissa does not begin with zero
*c. the base of the ordinate is not set at zero
d. two distributions are being presented simultaneously

19. Perhaps the most serious flaw in graphing data is due to

a. not placing frequencies on the abscissa
b. not placing raw scores on the ordinate
c. not placing the ordinate on the X axis
*d. not setting the base of the ordinate at zero

20. The following are all measures of central tendency, except

a. the mean
b. the median
*c. the sigma
d. the mode

21. The arithmetic average defines the

*a. mean
b. median
c. sigma
d. mode

22. The point above which half the scores fall and below which half the
scores fall, defines the

a. mean
*b. median
c. sigma
d. mode

23. The most frequently occurring score in the distribution defines the

a. mean   c. sigma
b. median   *d. mode

11

24. The mean is not overly affected by extreme scores, unless

    *a. the extreme scores are all in one direction
     b. .the extreme scores are in both directions
     c. the number of extreme scores is fewer then 5
     d. all of these

25. The fact that the mean IQ of college seniors is higher than that of freshmen is probably due to

     a. the fact that going to college increases the IQ
     b. the fact that there is a big IQ gain between the junior and senior years
     c. an incorrect interpretation of the data
    * d. the fact that the lower IQ freshmen tend to drop out of college and, therefore, never become seniors

26. Adding just one or two extreme scores to the high end of a distribution, has a great effect on

     a. the median, but not the mode
     b. the mode, but not the mean
    *c. the mean, but not the median
     d. none of these

27. Adding just one or two extreme scores to the low end of a distribution, has a great effect on

     a. the median, but not the mode
     b. the mode, but not the median
    *c. the mean, but not the median
     d. none of these

28. When the majority of scores are at the high end of the distribution, but there are a few extremely low scores, the distribution is

     a. bimodal
     b. multimodal
    *c. skewed left
     d. skewed right

29. When the mean lies to the right of the median, the distribution is probably

     a. bimodal
     b. multimodal
     c. skewed left
    *d. skewed right

30. When the median lies to the right of the mean, the distribution is probably

     a. bimodal
     b. multimodal
    *c. skewed left
     d. skewed right

31. When a distribution is skewed to the right,

   *a. the mode will be to the left of the median
   b. the mode will be to the right of the median
   c. the mode will be to the right of the mean
   d. the mode will be equal to the mean

Questions 32 through 37 are based on the following:

   In a certain community, the median per-family annual income is $22,000.
   The mean per-family income is $31,000, whereas the mode is $19,000.

32. The distribution of income scores is

   *a. skewed right
   b. skewed left
   c. skewed to the middle
   d. not skewed

33. The most appropriate measure of central tendency in this distribution
    would yield a vale of

   *a. $22,000
   b. $31,000
   c. $19,000
   d. none of these values would yield a measure of central tendency

34. If a new family were to move into the community with an annual income
    of $295,000, this would most affect

   *a. the mean
   b. the median
   c. the mode
   d. all of these

35. The annual income achieved by most of the families is

   a. $22,000
   b. $31,000
   *c. $19,000
   d. $11,000

36. The annual income which is surpassed by 50% of the families is

   *a. $22,000
   b. $31,000
   c. $19,000
   d. cannot tell from these data

37. The annual income which is surpassed by 90% of the families is

   a. $22,000
   b. $31,000
   c. $19,000
   *d. cannot tell from these data

38. Whenever a distribution is skewed left, the measure yielding the
    highest numerical value is always the

    a. mean
    b. median
    *c. mode
    d. percentile

39. When a skewed distribution tails off to the right, the distribution is

    *a. skewed right
    b. skewed left
    c. skewed to the center
    d. not skewed at all

40. In a histogram, the mode is always located

    a. under the shortest bar
    *b. under the tallest bar
    c. under the last bar to the right
    d. under the last bar to the left

41. A bimodal distribution often indicates

    a. that there will be two means
    b. that there will be two medians
    c. that the mean, median and mode have the same value
    *d. that two separate sub-groups have probably been measured

42. The most appropriate measure of central tendency in a bimodal distri-
    bution is the

    a. mean
    b. median
    *c. mode
    d. ordinate

43. When a distribution has two separate and distinct medians, then

    a. it is skewed right
    b. it is skewed left
    c. it is probably bimodal
    *d. a distribution can never have more than one median

44. The most appropriate measure of central tendency when the data are in
    ordinal form is

    a. the mean
    *b. the median
    c. the mode
    d. cannot tell without knowing whether the distribution is skewed

45. The most appropriate measure of central tendency when the data are in
    nominal form is

    a. the mean
    b. the median
    *c. the mode
    d. cannot tell without knowing whether the distribution is skewed

14

46. The most appropriate measure of central tendency when the data are in interval form is

    a. the mean
    b. the median
    c. the mode
   *d. cannot tell without knowing whether the distribution is skewed or bimodal

47. With ordinal data, the mean

    a. is always equal to the median
    b. is always equal to the mode
    c. is always higher than the mode
   *d. cannot be calculated

48. With interval data, a measure of central tendency which can be used is the

    a. mean
    b. median
    c. mode
   *d. all of these

49. With a fairly balanced distribution of interval scores, (neither skewed nor bimodal), the most appropriate measure of central tendency is the

   *a. mean
    b. median
    c. mode
    d. none of these

B. <u>True or False</u>: For the following, indicate T (True) or F (False)

50. A skewed right distribution has the mean to the left of the mode.   F

51. The median is always exactly half-way numerically between the highest and lowest scores.   F

52. The most appropriate measure of central tendency in a skewed right distribution is the median.   T

53. A positively skewed distribution is identical to a skewed right distribution.   T

54. Other things being equal, the mean is the most stable measure when the data form is nominal.   F

55. With a skewed left distribution, the median is <u>always</u> to the right of the mean.   T

56. With a skewed left distribution, the mode is <u>never</u> to the left of the mean.   T

57. All three measures of central tendency can be calculated when the data are in interval form.   T

58. On a frequency distribution curve, frequency of occurrence is always plotted on the abscissa.   F

59. One·should expect a distribution of personal income measures to be skewed to the right.   T

60. When the median is being calculated, it makes no difference whether one starts counting from the bottom or the top of the distribution.   T

61. If a positively skewed and negatively skewed distribution were combined, the resulting distribution would probably be bimodal.   T

C. For the following questions, calculate the values.

62. For the following set of scores, calculate the mean, median and mode: 11, 2, 3, 3, 7, 6.

    Ans. $\overline{X}$ = 5.33
        Mdn. = 4.50
        Mo. = 3.00

63. For the following set of scores, calculate the mean, median and mode: 20, 8, 18, 10, 15, 10, 13, 11.

    Ans. $\overline{X}$ = 13.13
        Mdn. = 12.00
        Mo. = 10.00

64. For the following set of scores, calculate the mean, median and mode: 3, 4, 7, 7, 5, 9.

    Ans. $\overline{X}$ = 5.83
        Mdn. = 6.00
        Mo. = 7.00

65. For the following set of scores, calculate the mean, median and mode: 5, 7, 3, 9, 4, 5, 5, 10, 9.

    Ans. $\overline{X}$ = 6.33
        Mdn. = 5.00
        Mo. = 5.00

66. For the following set of scores, calculate the mean, median and mode: 8, 8, 6, 7, 5, 9.

    Ans. $\overline{X}$ = 7.17
        Mdn. = 7.50
        Mo. = 8.00

67. For the following set of scores, calculate the mean, median and mode: 12, 1, 9, 7, 2, 4.

    Ans. $\overline{X}$ = 5.83
        Mdn. = 5.50
        Mo. = none

68. For the following set of scores, calculate the mean, median and mode: 10, 12, 9, 10, 10.

Ans. $\bar{X} = 10.20$
   Mdn. = 10.00
   Mo. = 10.00

69. For the following set of scores, calculate the mean, median and mode: 4, 3, 10, 10, 2.

Ans. $\bar{X} = 5.80$
   Mdn. = 4.00
   Mo. = 10.00

70. For the following set of scores, calculate the mean, median and mode: 7, 9, 9, 3, 11, 4, 2, 6.

Ans. $\bar{X} = 6.38$
   Mdn. = 6.50
   Mo. = 9.00

71. For the following set of scores, calculate the mean, median and mode: 9, 10, 12, 10, 10.

Ans. $\bar{X} = 10.20$
   Mdn. = 10.00
   Mo. = 10.00

72. For the following set of scores, calculate the mean, median and mode: 13, 9, 11, 3, 6, 8, 6, 5, 2, 10.

Ans. $\bar{X} = 7.30$
   Mdn. = 7.00
   Mo. = 6.00

73. For the following set of scores, calculate the mean, median and mode: 13, 12, 10, 12, 15, 11, 12, 8, 14.

Ans. $\bar{X} = 11.89$
   Mdn. = 12.00
   Mo. = 12.00

Questions 74 through 81 are based on the following:

Thirty-four members of a certain sorority were selected, and asked to indicate how many hours each had spent reading (for pleasure, not school work) during the previous week. The data are as follows: 50, 4, 10, 5, 5, 6, 7, 3, 5, 4, 4, 5, 6, 6, 7, 5, 8, 1, 8, 7, 5, 6, 10, 6, 8, 7, 7, 6, 5, 5, 4, 3, 4, 5.

74. Find the mean.

Ans. $\bar{X} = 6.97$

75. Find the median.

Ans. Mdn. = 5.50

76. Find the mode.

Ans. Mo. = 5.00

77. Which measure of central tendency is the highest?

Ans. Mean

78. Which is the lowest?

Ans. Mode

79. On the basis of your answers to numbers 77 and 78, describe the shape of the resulting distribution.

Ans. Slightly skewed to the right.

80. What would the mean and median have been if the highest score had been a 12 instead of a 50?

Ans. $\bar{X}$ = 5.85, Mdn. = 5.50

81. Set up these data in two columns as a frequency distribution, using the original set of scores.

Ans.

X	f
50	1
10	2
8	3
7	5
6	6
5	9
4	5
3	2
1	1

CHAPTER 3
VARIABILITY

A. <u>Multiple Choice Items</u>

1. The concept of "individual differences" may best be described by

    a. the mode
    b. the median
    c. the measures of central tendency
    *d. the measures of variability

2. The difference between the highest and lowest score in any distribution is called

    a. the deviation score
    b. the standard deviation
    *c. the range
    d. none of these

3. Of the following, the measure(s) of variability is (are),

    a. the range
    b. the standard deviation
    c. the mode
    *d. a and b, but not c

4. One major defect of the range is that

    a. it includes the entire width of the distribution
    *b. it is based on only two scores
    c. it is not a measure of variability
    d. all of these

5. The measure of the entire width of the distribution is called the

    *a. range
    b. percentile
    c. quartile
    d. a and b, but not c

6. When new scores are added to any distribution, chances are great that the range will

    a. remain unaffected
    b. be reduced
    *c. be increased
    d. new scores may <u>never</u> be added to a distribution

7. Specific points may be located on any distribution by using the

    a. percentile
    b. quartile
    c. decile
    *d. all of these

8. A score which is at the 95th percentile must exceed

   a. at least 5% of the scores
   *b. at least 95% of the scores
   c. at least 45% of the scores
   d. at least the lowest 4% of scores

9. When a student takes a 600-item standardized test and is told he/she is at the 70th percentile, it means that the student

   a. answered 30% of the items correctly
   b. answered more than 70% of the items correctly
   c. answered exactly 420 items correctly
   *d. none of these

10. A score which falls at the 50th percentile must <u>always</u> be at the

    a. mean
    b. mode
    *c. median
    d. none of these

11. If 50% of the cases fall above a given point, then 50% must also fall

    *a. below that point
    b. between the mean and median
    c. between the first and fifth deciles
    d. none of these, since the distribution can never account for 100% of the cases

12. The first quartile coincides with the

    a. first percentile
    *b. twenty-fifth percentile
    c. seventy-fifth percentile
    d. median

13. The interquartile range lies between

    a. the median and the third quartile
    b. the median and the first quartile
    c. the median and the lowest score in the distribution
    *d. the first and third quartiles

14. The fifth decile coincides with the

    a. 50th percentile
    b. 2nd quartile
    c. median
    *d. all of these

15. The third quartile falls between the

    a. 1st and 5th deciles   b. 2nd and 3rd deciles
    c. 4th and 6th deciles   *d. 7th and 8th deciles

16. The interdecile range lies between the

    a. 3rd and 7th deciles
    b. 2nd and 8th deciles
  *c. 1st and 9th deciles
    d. median and the 10th decile

17. The interquartile range includes the middle-most

    a. 25% of the cases
  *b. 50% of the cases
    c. 75% of the cases
    d. 95% of the cases

18. Of the following, which should not be calculated when the data are in ordinal form?

    a. median
    b. quartile
    c. decile
  *d. mean

19. Of the following, which can be calculated even though the data are in ordinal form?

    a. interquartile range
    b. interdecile range
    c. the middle-most 50% of the scores
  *d. all of these

20. The standard deviation is a measure of

  *a. how far all the scores vary from the mean
    b. how far the middle-most 50% of cases vary from the mean
    c. how far the highest and lowest scores vary from each other
    d. central tendency

21. The standard deviation must always be calculated with reference to the

    a. decile
    b. median
    c. mode
  *d. mean

22. The more heterogeneous the distribution of scores,

    a. the smaller the standard deviation
  *b. the larger the standard deviation
    c. the more the distribution tends to be skewed
    d. the greater the chance of excluding extreme scores

23. The deviation score is

    a. exactly the same as the standard deviation
    b. only the same as the standard deviation when variability is small
    c. only the same as the standard deviation when variability is large
  *d. the difference between the raw score and the mean

24. When a deviation score has a negative value, then

     *a. the raw score is below the mean
      b. the raw score is above the mean
      c. the raw score equals the mean
      d. none of these, since deviation scores can never be negative

25. When the standard deviation has a negative value, then

      a. most scores were above the mean
      b. most scores were below the mean
      c. the distribution is skewed
     *d. none of these, since the standard deviation can never be negative

26. If the value of the standard deviation is greater than the value
    of the range, then

      a. the distribution is heterogeneous
      b. the distribution is homogeneous
      c. the distribution is skewed
     *d. none of these, since the standard deviation must always be less
          than the range

27. If two football running-backs have the same yards-per-carry average, but
    player A has a larger standard deviation than player B, then

      a. player A has a greater chance of making a long gain
      b. player A has a greater chance of being caught for a loss
      c. player A is the more consistent runner
     *d. a and b, but not c

28. Of two golfers, each of whom drives the ball the same average distance,
    the one with the smaller standard deviation would be

     *a. the more consistent
      b. the less consistent
      c. the one more apt, on a given shot, to drive the ball further
      d. none of these, since they both drive the same average distance

29. The higher the value of the standard deviation, the higher the

      a. percentile
      b. decile
      c. quartile
     *d. none of these

30. If two distributions have the same mean, then they must also have the
    same

      a. median
      b. mode
      c. standard deviation
     *d. none of these

31. A distribution with a large standard deviation must also have a large

      a. number of scores near the mean
      b. number of scores near the median

*c.　variance
　　　d.　none of these

32.　The standard deviation demands that the data form be at least

　　　a.　nominal
　　　b.　ordinal
　　　*c.　interval
　　　d.　none of these, since the standard deviation has no data-scale
　　　　　requirements

33.　The variance is equal to

　　　*a.　the standard deviation squared
　　　b.　the square-root of the standard deviation
　　　c.　twice the standard deviation
　　　c.　none of these

34.　You know you've made a math error whenever the standard deviation is

　　　a.　smaller than the variance
　　　*b.　negative
　　　c.　smaller than the range
　　　d.　b and c, but not a

35.　The only time the standard deviation may equal zero, is when

　　　a.　the range is less than 50
　　　*b.　every score in the distribution is the same
　　　c.　the range is negative
　　　d.　none of these, since the standard deviation may never
　　　　　be equal to zero

36.　The only time the range may equal zero, is when

　　　a.　the standard deviation is less than 1.00
　　　*b.　every score in the distribution is the same
　　　c.　the standard deviation is negative
　　　d.　the interdecile range is skewed to the left

37.　A platykurtic distribution always has

　　　a.　a relatively small standard deviation
　　　*b.　a relatively large standard deviation
　　　c.　a standard deviation of zero
　　　d.　a few extreme scores at just one end of the distribution

38.　The term which defines the flatness or peakedness of a curve is

　　　*a.　kurtosis
　　　b.　range-values
　　　c.　central tendency
　　　d.　homoscedasticity

39.　When most scores cluster closely around the mean, the curve is

　　　a.　asymmetrical　　　　　　　c.　shaped like a U
　　　b.　platykurtic　　　　　　　*d.　leptokurtic

40. The smaller the standard deviation

    *a. the more leptokurtic the resulting curve
    b. ·the more mesokurtic the resulting curve
    c. the more platykurtic the resulting curve
    d. the higher the chance of the curve being bimodal

41. When the range equals approximately 6 times the standard deviation, then the curve is most likely to be

    a. skewed
    b. leptokurtic
    c. platykurtic
   *d. mesokurtic

42. If two distributions have the same mean and same range, then they must also

    a. have the same standard deviation
    b. when graphed, have the same kurtosis
    c. have the same variance
   *d. none of these

43. When a very homogeneous set of scores is graphed, the resulting curve is

    a. platykurtic
   *b. leptokurtic
    c. mesokurtic
    d. bimodal

44. If the range on a mesokurtic distribution is equal to 60, then the standard deviation will be approximately equal to

   *a. 10
    b. 360
    c. .17
    d. impossible to determine from the facts given

45. Of the following, indicate which is not a measure of variability

    a. range
   *b. percentile
    c. standard deviation
    d. variance

Questions 46 through 54 will be bases on the following:

A researcher gives IQ tests to a large group of adults, and discovers that the mean, median and mode all equal 100. The highest score in the group was 130 and the lowest was 70. Between IQ's of 75 and 125, 80% of the group was found, and 50% were found between IQ's of 90 and 110. The shape of the graphed distribution was mesokurtic.

46. The range was equal to

   *a. 60
    b. 50
    c. 20
    d. 0

47. The interdecile range was equal to

   a. 60
   *b. 50
   c. 20
   d. 0

48. The interquartile range was equal to

   a. 60
   b. 50
   *c. 20
   d. 0

49. The fifth decile coincided with an IQ of

   a. 70
   b. 75
   *c. 100
   d. 125

50. The second quartile coincided with an IQ of

   a. 70
   b. 75
   *c. 100
   d. 125

51. The ninth decile coincided with an IQ of

   a. 75
   b. 100
   *c. 125
   d. 130

52. The first decile coincided with an IQ of

   *a. 75
   b. 90
   c. 100
   d. 130

53. The third quartile coincided with an IQ of

   a. 75
   b. 90
   *c. 110
   d. 125

54. The standard deviation was equal to approximately

   a. 0
   *b. 10
   c. 15
   d. cannot tell, since not enough information is provided

55. The variance was equal to

    a. 0
  *b. 100
    c. 3.87
    d. 225

B. <u>True of False</u>: For the following, indicate T (True) or F (False)

56. The distribution with the largest standard deviation   F
necessarily has the largest range.

57. Two distributions may have the same mean, and yet have   T
different standard deviations.

58. A negative standard deviation indicates that most of the   F
scores were below the mean

59. The standard deviation may only be computed with   T
reference to the mean.

60. A leptokurtic distribution has a relatively small   T
standard deviation.

61. The interquartile range includes only the middle-most   F
25% of the distribution.

62. The standard deviation of any distribution must always   F
equal one-sixth of the range.

63. The median must always coincide with the fifth decile.   T

64. If you were to receive a score on an exam which placed   T
you at the 90th percentile, then 90% of those taking
the test did worse than you.

65. The higher the value of the standard deviation, then   T
the more the scores are spread out around the mean.

66. The higher the value of the mean, then the higher the   F
value of the range.

67. When the vast majority of scores cluster tightly around   T
the mean, the graphed distribution is leptokurtic.

68. The interdecile range includes the middle-most 90% of   F
all the scores.

69. The smallest possible standard deviation is equal to zero.   T

70. Kurtosis refers to the flatness or peakedness of the curve.   T

71. The standard deviation may never be larger than the range.   T

72. If a student takes a test and gets 70% of the items right,   F
then the student's score is at the 70th percentile.

73. The interquartile range is more narrow than is the   T
interdecile range.

C. For the following questions, calculate the values.

74. For the following set of scores, calculate the mean, range and
standard deviation: 1, 2, 14, 13, 3.

Ans. $\overline{X}$ = 6.60
R = 13
SD = 5.68

75. For the following set of scores, calculate the mean, range and
standard deviation: 12, 2, 5, 9, 11, 10, 10, 4.

Ans. $\overline{X}$ = 7.88
R = 10
SD = 3.43

76. For the following set of scores, calculate the mean, range and
standard deviation: 10, 8, 12, 3, 6, 7, 2, 10.

Ans. $\overline{X}$ = 7.25
R = 10
SD = 3.27

77. For the following set of scores, calculate the mean, range and
standard deviation: 9, 9, 11, 1, 7, 2.

Ans. $\overline{X}$ = 6.50
R = 10
SD = 3.73

78. For the following set of scores, calculate the mean, range and
standard deviation: 12, 10, 2, 7, 9, 10.

Ans. $\overline{X}$ = 8.33
R = 10
SD = 3.21

79. For the following set of scores, calculate the mean, range and
standard deviation: 6, 13, 14, 12, 10, 5.

Ans. $\overline{X}$ = 10.00
R = 9
SD = 3.42

80. For the following set of scores, calculate the mean, median, mode
and standard deviation: 13, 14, 12, 15, 10, 7, 12.

Ans. $\overline{X}$ = 11.86
Mdn.= 12.00
Mo. = 12.00
SD = 2.46

81. For the following set of scores, calculate the mean, median, mode
and standard deviation: 10, 3, 10, 2, 5.

Ans. $\overline{X}$ = 6.00
Mdn. = 5.00
Mo. = 10.00
SD = 3.41

82. For the following set of scores, calculate the mean, median, mode and standard deviation: 5, 10, 10, 5, 5, 2, 3, 5, 9, 7.

Ans. $\overline{X}$ = 6.10
     Mdn. = 5.00
     Mo. = 5.00
     SD = 2.66

83. For the following set of scores, calculate the mean, median, mode and standard deviation: 14, 9, 7, 7, 10, 4, 7.

Ans. $\overline{X}$ = 8.29
     Mdn. = 7.00
     Mo. = 7.00
     SD = 2.90

84. For the following set of scores, calculate the mean, median, mode and standard deviation: 11, 10, 10, 7, 6.

Ans. $\overline{X}$ = 8.80
     Mdn. = 10.00
     Mo. = 10.00
     SD = 1.94

85. For the following set of scores, calculate the mean, median, mode and standard deviation: 13, 10, 10, 3, 11, 12, 9, 10, 8, 10.

Ans. $\overline{X}$ = 9.60
     Mdn. = 10.00
     Mo. = 10.00
     SD = 2.58

For questions 86 through 91, use the following data:

A researcher wished to evaluate the operating life of a certain brand of storage battery. A group of 30, brand-new batteries was selected and placed in 30 identical automobiles. The lights in each automobile were then turned on (without running the engines), and the length of time before the batteries were fully discharged (lights went out) was recorded. The scores, in hours, were: 15, 10, 20, 18, 18, 11, 11, 11, 11, 12, 12, 12, 10, 9, 9, 8, 9, 9, 11, 11, 11, 15, 12, 12, 12, 10, 12, 12, 15, 12.

86. Calculate the mean.

Ans. $\overline{X}$ = 12.00

87. Calculate the median.

Ans. Mdn. = 11.50

88. Calculate the mode.

Ans. MO. = 12.00

89. Calculate the range.

Ans. R = 12

90. Calculate the standard deviation.

Ans. SD = 2.79

91. Calculate the variance.

Ans. V = SD^2 = 7.78

CHAPTER 4
THE NORMAL CURVE AND z SCORES

A. Multiple Choice Items

1. The discovery of the normal curve is popularly credited to

    a. Blaise Pascal
    b. Henry Gossett
    c. Pat Cushing
    *d. Karl Gauss

2. The normal curve is

    a. symmetrical
    b. unimodal
    c. asymptotic to the abscissa
    *d. all of these

3. A bimodal distribution may never be

    a. symmetrical
    b. a frequency distribution
    *c. normal
    d. all of these

4. A normal curve always has

    *a. a greater frequency of scores around the center than in the tails
    b. a greater frequency of scores in the tails than around the center
    c. a greater frequency of scores above the mean than below the mean
    d. a greater frequency of scores below the mean than above the mean

5. Under the normal curve

    a. the mean lies to the right of the median
    b. the mode lies to the left of the mean
    c. the median lies to the left of the mode
    *d. none of these

6. Every normal curve is

    *a. a frequency distribution curve
    b. leptokurtic
    c. platykurtic
    d. skewed to the left

7. When the normal curve is plotted according to standard deviation units,
    each having a value of 1.00, it is called

    a. platykurtic
    b. leptokurtic
    *c. the standard normal curve
    d. the deviation curve

8. Under the normal curve, 68% of the cases always fall

    a. above the mean
    *b. between ± 1 standard deviation units from the mean

c. between ± 2 standard deviation units from the mean
d. all of these, depending on the particular shape of the curve

9. Under the normal curve, 50% of the cases always fall

   a. below the mean
   b. above the mean
   c. below the median
*d. all of these

10. When more than 34% of the cases under the curve fall between the
     mean and a z score of ± 1, then

   a. 68% of the cases fall below the mean
   b. the curve cannot be symmetrical
*c. the curve cannot be normal
   d. none of these

11. When the mean and median do not coincide, then

*a. the curve cannot be normal
   b. the curve cannot be skewed
   c. the curve cannot be unimodal
   d. the curve cannot be a frequency distribution curve

12. Under the normal curve the 50th percentile always falls at the

   a. mean
   b. median
   c. mode
*d. all of these

13. Under the normal curve, between the z scores of +1 and +2, there
     are always

   a. 68% of the cases
   b. 95% of the cases
*c. 13.50% of the cases
   d. sometimes a, and sometimes b, but never c

14. Under the normal curve, the percentage of cases falling above a
     z score of +3, is

   a. 68%
   b. 95%
   c. more than 1%
*d. less than 1%

15. Under the normal curve, between z scores of ± 10, there are always

   a. 100% of the cases
   b. 95% of the cases
   c. 68% of the cases
*d. more than 99%, but less than 100% of the cases

16. When a z score falls to the left of the mean

*a. it must always be given a minus sign
   b. it must always be greater than 1

c. it must always be less than 1
d. none of these, since z scores never fall to the left
of the mean

17. If an IQ distribution is normal and has a mean of 100 and a standard
deviation of 15, then 68% of all those taking the test scored between
IQ's of

    a. 100 and 115
    b. 85 and 100
    c. 92.5 and 107.5
*d. 85 and 115

18. If an IQ distribution is normal and has a mean of 100 and a standard
deviation of 15, then 99% of all those taking the test scored between
IQ's of

    a. 0 and 150
*b. 55 and 145
    c. 85 and 115
    d. 92.5 and 107.5

19. Under the normal curve, when the z score is equal to +1, then

    a. the standard deviation of the sistribution of raw scores must
equal 15
    b. the standard deviation of the distribution of raw scores must
equal 10
    c. the standard deviation of the distribution of raw scores must
equal 0
*d. none of these

20. Under the normal curve, if the mean of the distribution of raw
scores is equal to 68, then its equivalent z score is equal to

    a. 10
    b. 1
*c. 0
    d. none of these

21. Assume a normal distribution of height scores, with a mean of 68"
and a standard deviation of 3", then

    a. 68% of the cases must fall between 65" and 71"
    b. 50% of the cases must fall below 68"
    c. 68% of the cases must fall at exactly 68"
*d. a and b, but not c

22. The larger the absolute value of the z score (regardless of its sign),
then

    a. the higher its equivalent raw score
    b. the lower its equivalen raw score
*c. the further it is from the mean
    d. the closer its equivalent raw score must be to the mean

23. The z score provides information regarding how far a given raw score is

   *a. .from the mean in units of standard deviation
    b. from the mean in percentage units
    c. from the lowest score in percentile units
    d. from the highest score in percentile units

24. On any normal distribution the 50th percentile corresponds with a
    z score of

   *a. 0
    b. 50
    c. 68
    d. +1

25. Under the normal curve, if a given raw score falls at the 84th
    percentile, then its equivalent z score must be equal to

    a. the mean
    b. 0
   *c. +1
    d. +2

26. Under the normal curve, any percentile of less than 50 must correspond
    to a

   *a. negative z score
    b. raw score of less than 50
    c. z score of less than 1
    d. z score of 0

27. The closer a given z score is to 0, then the closer it is

    a. to the tails of the curve
   *b. to the mean of the distribution
    c. to the 68th percentile
    d. to a 0% frequency

28. Under the normal curve, the only point where the frequency of
    cases is zero is

    a. between the mean and a z score of +1
    b. beyond a z score of +1
    c. beyond a z score of +2
   *d. none of these

29. The higher a given point on the normal curve is, then

   *a. the higher the frequency of scores below that point
    b. the lower the frequency of scores below that point
    c. the closer the point is to the abscissa
    d. the higher the resulting raw score

30. A negative z score means that

   *a. the raw score is below the mean
    b. the mean is below the raw score
    c. the distribution is skewed left
    d. none of these, since it is impossible to get a negative z score

31. Under the normal curve, the mean falls at the 50th percentile only when

    a.   the mean of the raw score distribution is equal to 50
    b.   the mean of the raw score distribution is equal to 100
    c.   the mean of the raw score distribution is unknown
 *d.   none of these, since under the normal curve the mean falls
       at the 50th percentile

32. Under the normal curve, the relationship between a specific z score and the percentage of cases falling between it and the mean

    a.   depends on the size of the standard deviation
    b.   depends on the value of the mean
    c.   depends on the value of the raw score
 *d.   is a constant

For questions 33 through 42 use the following:

The mean on a given normal distribution of raw scores is 500 with a standard deviation of 100.

33. A z score of +1 corresponds with a raw score of

    a.   200
    b.   400
    c.   500
 *d.   600

34. The 84th percentile corresponds with a raw score of

    a.   250
    b.   500
 *c.   600
    d.   800

35. The 49th percentile must be below a raw score of

 *a.   500
    b.   400
    c.   300
    d.   200

36. Between the raw scores of 400 and 600, there must be

    a.   50% of the scores
    b.   34% of the scores
 *c.   68% of the scores
    d.   95% of the scores

37. A raw score of 200 would translate into a z score of

 *a.   -3
    b.   -1
    c.   +1
    d.   +2

38. A raw score of 500 would translate into a z score of

   a. -3
   b. -1
   c. -.01
   *d. 0

39. Approximately 68% of all the scores would fall

   *a. between raw scores of 400 and 600
   b. between raw scores of 200 and 500
   c. between raw scores of 500 and 600
   d. above a raw score of 700

40. The 50th percentile would yield a raw score of

   a. 400
   b. 450
   *c. 500
   d. 568

41. The 50th percentile would yield a z score of

   a. -1
   b. +500
   c. above +1
   *d. 0

42. Over 50% of all the scores would fall above a raw score of

   a. 568
   b. 534
   c. 501
   *d. 499

43. When a given point under the normal curve is 1.54 standard deviation units above the mean, then

   a. its percentile is 15.4
   b. its percentile is 1.54
   *c. its z score is +1.54
   d. both a and c, but not b

44. All percentiles of less than 50 must necessarily

   a. fall below the raw score mean
   b. yield negative z scores
   c. fall to the left of the z score mean
   *d. all of these

45. A positive z score must always yield a percentile which is

   *a. above 50
   b. below 50
   c. between 40 and 60
   d. above 100

46. Percentiles always indicate

    *a. the percentage of cases falling below a given point
    b. the percentage of cases falling above a given point
    c. the percentage of cases falling between a given z score
       and the mean
    d. the percentage of cases falling above a given z score

47. A z score of +3 corresponds with a

    a. percentile of 3
    b. percentile of 53
    c. percentile of 103
    *d. raw score which is 3 standard deviation units above the mean

48. For a z score of 1.35 the z score table indicates a percentage value
    of 41.15. This means that

    a. 41.15% of the cases fell below a z score of +1.35
    b. 41.15% of the cases fell above a z score of +1.35
    c. 41.15% of the cases fell between z scores of +1.35
    *d. 41.15% of the cases fell between a z score of +1.35 and the mean

49. The z score table always gives, as a direct read-out, the percentage
    of cases falling

    *a. between a given z score and the mean
    b. below a negative z score
    c. above a positive z score
    d. none of these

50. The percentage values on the z score table are only valid when

    a. the z scores are positive
    b. the raw score mean equals 50
    c. the raw score mean is greater than 50
    *d. the distribution is normal

51. The difference between z scores and standard scores is that

    a. z scores can never be negative, whereas standard deviation
       scores always are
    b. z scores can only be calculated with reference to the mean,
       whereas standard scores relate to the median
    c. z scores can only be calculated with reference to the
       standard deviation, whereas standard scores relate to the variance
    *d. none of these, since z scores are standard scores

52. Every distribution of z scores has a

    *a. mean of zero and a standard deviation of 1
    b. mean of 50 and a standard deviation of 10
    c. mean of 100 and a standard deviation of 15
    d. none of these, since every distribution of z scores is different

53. The fact that the normal distribution is asymptotic to the abscissa means that

    a. its curve must be symmetrical
    b. its curve must yield both positive and negative values
  *c. its curve may never touch the abscissa
    d. its curve must always touch the abscissa

54. The difference between the raw score and the mean when divided by the standard deviation yields the

    a. normal curve
    b. percentile
    c. first moment of the curve
  *d. z score

55. The only time a z score can be negative is when

    a. the raw score is higher than the mean
  *b. the raw score is lower than the mean
    c. the standard deviation is negative
    d. the standard deviation is equal to 0

56. When the standard deviation of the raw score distribution is negative, the resulting z score must be

    a. negative
    b. equal to 0
    c. positive
  *d. none of these, since the standard deviation can never be negative

57. Between two negative z scores there must always be

  *a. fewer than 50% of the cases
    b. more than 50% of the cases
    c. exactly 50% of the cases
    d. none of these, since 0% must always fall between negative z scores

58. Anytime a z score yields a percentile which is greater than 50, then

    a. the z score must be positive
    b. the raw score must be higher than the mean
    c. the z score must be greater than 0
  *d. all of these

59. The z score for any raw score may be found by

  *a. subtracting the mean from the raw score and dividing by the standard deviation
    b. subtracting the raw score from the mean and dividing by the standard deviation
    c. subtracting the raw score from 100 and dividing by 15
    d. none of these, since raw scores cannot be converted into z scores

60. Whenever a given raw score coincides exactly with the mean, the resulting z score, regardless of the size of the standard deviation, must be

   *a. equal to 0
   b. positive
   c. equal to 50
   d. none of these, since in this case, the z score cannot be found

B. True or False: For the following, indicate T (True) or F (False)

61. Between z scores of ± 3 over 99% of the cases will be found.   T

62. A negative z score always yields a percentile of less than 50.   T

63. A negative z score always means that the raw score is less than
    the mean.   T

64. Fewer than 50% of the cases may ever fall between two z scores
    of the same sign.   T

65. Whenever the mean of a raw score distribution is less than 50,
    the z score must be negative.   F

66. The mean of the z score distribution must always equal 0.   T

67. A frequency distribution curve may be symmetrical without being
    normal.   T

68. On a normal distribution the mean always lies to the right of
    the mode.   F

69. There are more cases which fall above a z score of +2 than
    there are falling below it.   F

70. Under the normal curve, the further to the right on the
    abscissa, the greater the number of cases.   F

71. When any frequency distribution curve is symmetrical, it must,
    by definition, also be normal.   F

72. The normal curve is mesokurtic.   T

73. All percentiles above 50 must yield negative z scores.   F

74. The normal distribution curve is unimodal.   T

75. A positive z score always results when the raw score is greater
    than the mean.   T

76. A positive z score may only occur when the mean of the raw score
    distribution is greater than 50.   F

77. A percentile of greater than 50 may only occur when the mean
    of the raw score distribution is greater than 50.   F

78. Regardless of the size of the raw score mean or standard deviation, a z score of +1 always means that the raw score is exactly one, full standard deviation unit above the mean.　　T

79. Raw scores may never be converted into z scores unless the raw score mean is equal to 0.　　F

80. The standard score is synonomous with the raw score.　　F

81. On a normal distribution the mean and median coincide.　　T

C. For the following questions, calculate the values.

82. Percentage of scores falling between a z of 1.54 and the mean

    Ans. 43.83%

83. Percentage of scores falling between a z of -1.73 and the mean

    Ans. 45.82%

84. Percentage of scores falling between a z of .56 and the mean

    Ans. 21.23%

85. Percentage of scores falling below a z of 2.56

    Ans. 99.48%

86. Percentage of scores falling below a z of 1.44

    Ans. 92.51%

87. Percentage of scores falling below a z of -.24

    Ans. 40.52%

88. Percentage of scores falling above a z of 1.44

    Ans. 7.49%

89. Percentage of scores falling above a z of -.67

    Ans. 74.86%

90. Percentage of scores falling between z's of -.80 and +.80

    Ans. 57.62%

91. Percentage of scores falling between z's of .50 and 1.25

    Ans. 20.29%

92. Percentage of scores falling between z's of -.53 and +.84

    Ans. 50.14%

93. Percentage of scores falling between z's of -.15 and -.44

   Ans. 11.04%

94. Percentage of scores falling between z's of -.80 and -2.00

   Ans. 18.91%

95. On a normal distribution with a mean of 200 and a standard deviation of 50, what percentage of cases will fall between raw scores of 185 and 195?

   Ans. 7.81%

96. On a normal distribution with a mean of 500 and a standard deviation of 97, what percentage of cases will fall between 470 and 550?

   Ans. 32.02%

97. On a normal distribution with a mean of 100 and a standard deviation of 17, what percentage of cases will fall between 84 and 93?

   Ans. 16.73%

98. On a normal distribution with a mean of 22.50 and a standard deviation of 6.20, what percentage of cases will fall between 24 and 28?

   Ans. 21.85%

99. On a normal distribution with a mean of 150 and a standard deviation of 17, what percentage of cases will fall between 129 and 145?

   Ans. 27.84%

100. On a normal distribution with a mean of 100 and a standard deviation of 7, what percentage of cases will fall between 105 and 110?

   Ans. 16.25%

101. On a normal distribution with a mean of 150 and a standard deviation of 15, what percentage of cases will fall at 140 or higher?

   Ans. 74.86%

102. On a normal distribution with a mean of 160 and a standard deviation of 16.28, what percentage of cases will fall between 145 and 166?

   Ans. 46.55%

For questions 103 through 108, use the following:

   The mean weight among a group of female high school seniors is 120 lbs., with a standard deviation of 16.49 lbs. Assuming a normal distribution, find the percentiles for the following weight scores.

103. 125 lbs.

   Ans. 61.79, or 62nd percentile

104. 140 lbs.

    Ans. 88.69, or 89th percentile

105. 115 lbs.

    Ans. 38.21, or 38th percentile

106. 90 lbs.

    Ans. 3.44, or 3rd percentile

107. 107 lbs.

    Ans. 21.48, or 21st percentile

108. 165 lbs.

    Ans. 99.68, or 100th percentile

A. Multiple Choice Items

1. When converting a z score into a raw score, anytime the z score is negative in sign

   a. so too will be the raw score
   b. so too will be the mean
   c. so too will be the standard deviation
   *d. the value of the raw score will be less than the mean

2. When converting a z score into a raw score, anytime the z score is positive in sign

   a. so too will be the raw score
   b. so too will be the mean
   *c. the value of the raw score will be greater than the mean
   d. none of these, since the conversion can only be made when z is negative

3. A z score of -1.50 indicates that the raw score is

   a. one and one-half percentage points below the mean
   *b. one and one-half standard deviation units below the mean
   c. one and one-half raw score units below the mean
   d. negative

4. A z score of +3.00, means that

   *a. the raw score is exactly 3 standard deviation units above the mean
   b. the raw score is exactly percentage points above the mean
   c. the raw score is exactly 3 raw score units above the mean
   d. none of these

5. On a normal distribution, percentiles may be converted into raw scores

   *a. by first translating the percentile into a z score
   b. by first translating the mean into a standard score
   c. by first translating the percentile into the decile equivalent
   d. all of these

6. Any percentile which is greater than 50 will convert into a raw score

   a. which is greater than 50
   b. which is to the left of the mean
   *c. which is greater than the mean
   d. which is larger than the value of the percentile

7. A percentile rank of 95 indicates that

   a. 95% of the distribution is above it
   b. 45% of the distribution is above it
   *c. 95% of the distribution is below it
   d. 45% of the distribution is below it

8. A percentile rank of 45 indicates that

   *a. it is 5 percentage points below the mean
   b. it is 45 percentage points below the mean
   c. it is 95 percentage points below the mean
   d. it is above the mean

9. A percentile rank of 85 indicates that

   a. 15% of the distribution is below it
   b. 35% of the distribution is below it
   *c. 35% of the distribution is between it and the mean
   d. it is below the mean

10. When converting percentiles into z scores, it is essential to know

    a. the value of the mean
    b. the value of the standard deviation
    c. the value of the raw score
    *d. the percentage of cases falling between the given percentile and
        the mean

11. Whenever the value of the standard deviation is positive, then

    a. the z score must be positive
    b. the percentile must be greater than 50
    c. the raw score must be above the mean
    *d. none of these, since the standard deviation is always positive

12. Whenever the value of the z score is positive, then

    a. the percentile must be greater than 50
    b. the raw score must be greater than the mean
    c. neither of these, since the z score is always positive
    *d. both a and b, but not c

13. All z scores falling to the left of the mean

    *a. must be given negative signs
    b. must result in negative percentiles
    c. must result in negative raw scores
    d. none of these

14. Whenever the percentage values in the z score table indicate an
    absolute tie

    *a. use the higher of the two z scores
    b. use the lower of the two z scores
    c. use the z score which is closest to the mean
    d. the z score cannot be used

15. If someone were to score at the 84th percentile, the resulting z score
    would be approximately

    a. .50
    *b. 1.00
    c. .34
    d. none of these, since a percentile never yields a z score

16. If someone were to score at the 16th percentile, the resulting z score would be approximately

   a. -.50
   *b. -1.00
   c. -.34
   d. none of these, since a percentile never yields a z score

17. On a normal distribution, the value of the standard deviation can be found from a knowledge of the

   a. mean, median and mode
   *b. mean, z score and raw score
   c. z score, raw score and percentile
   d. curve's kurtosis

18. If the mean of a normal distribution were equal to 100, and a raw score of 99 was found to be at the 10th percentile, then

   *a. the standard deviation must be extremely small
   b. the standard deviation must be extremely large
   c. the standard deviation must be less than the z score
   d. the standard deviation could not be calculated from this information

19. If the standard deviation of a normal distribution were equal to 15 and someone had a raw score of 122, which fell at the 90th percentile, then the mean

   a. must be greater than 122
   *b. must be less than 122
   c. must be between 90 and 122
   d. could not be found from the above information

20. Whenever the z score equation is used in order to calculate the mean, the mean must always be greater than the raw score

   *a. when the raw score has a percentile value of less than 50
   b. when the raw score has a percentile value of greater than 50
   c. when the raw score is negative
   d. when the z score is positive

21. Whenever the z score equation is used in order to calculate the mean, the mean must always be less than the raw score

   a. when the raw score has a percentile value of less than 50
   b. when the raw score is positive
   c. when the z score is negative
   *d. when the raw score has a percentile value of greater than 50

22. The percentile value for a given raw score must always be at least 50 whenever

   a. the mean is greater than the raw score
   b. the raw score is more than 1 percentage point away from the mean
   c. the equivalent z score is greater than 50
   *d. the equivalent z score is positive

23. When a raw score translates into a negative z score, the resulting percentile must be

    a. negative
    b. greater than 50
  *c. less than 50
    d. none of these

24. When a raw score translates into a negative z score, then the mean of the distribution

  *a. must be higher than the raw score
    b. must be lower than the raw score
    c. must fall above the 50th percentile
    d. must fall below the 50th percentile

25. In a normal distribution, the mean falls above the 50th percentile only when

    a. the z score is positive
    b. the raw score is negative
    c. the raw score is below the 50th percentile
  *d. none of these

26. The T score can only be used

    a. when the mean of the raw score distribution equals 50
    b. when the z score distribution is no longer normal
    c. when the mean of the raw score distribution is 100
  *d. when the distribution is normal

27. The value of the mean of the T score distribution is always equal to

    a. the value of the raw score mean
    b. the value of the z score mean
    c. the value of the standard deviation
  *d. 50

28. The range of the T score distribution always equals approximately

    a. 50
  *b. 60
    c. 30
    d. the same value as the range of the raw score distribution

29. A T score of 60 is equal to a z score of

    a. 0
    b. +2
  *c. +1
    d. 50

30. A T score of 30 is equal to a z score of

  *a. -2
    b. +2
    c. +1
    d. 0

31. When a raw score converts to a percentile of greater than 50, then the resulting T score must be

    a. negative
    b. equal to 10
    c. equal to the z score
  *d. greater than 50

32. A T score of 60 is exactly

  *a. one standard deviation unit above the mean
    b. ten standard deviation units above the mean
    c. ten standard deviation units below the mean
    d. the same as a percentile rank of 60

33. The value of the standard deviation of the T distribution is equal to

    a. the standard deviation of z
    b. the standard deviation of the raw score distribution
    c. the standard deviation of the raw score distribution, divided by 10
  *d. 10

34. If the mean of the raw score distribution equals 68 with a standard deviation of 3, then a person with a raw score of 65 would have a T score of

    a. 60
    b. 50
    c. 47
  *d. 40

35. If the mean of the raw score distribution equals 120 with a standard deviation of 5, then a raw score of 130 would equal a T score of

    a. 55
    b. 60
  *c. 70
    d. 30

36. A raw score which is at the 50th percentile translates into a T score of

  *a. 50
    b. 10
    c. 70
    d. cannot tell from information given

37. When the standard deviation of the raw score distribution equals 10, then the mean of the raw score distribution must equal

    a. 50
    b. 100
    c. 15
  *d. cannot tell from information given

38. The T score distribution always assumes a

    *a. mean of 50 and an SD of 10
    b. mean of 100 and an SD of 15
    c. mean of 0 and an SD of 1
    d. none of these

39. The z score distribution always assumes a

    a. mean of 50 and an SD of 10
    b. mean of 100 and an SD of 15
    *c. mean of 0 and an SD of 1
    d. none of these

40. The raw score distribution always assumes a

    a. mean of 50 and an SD of 10
    b. mean of 100 and an SD of 15
    c. mean of 0 and an SD of 1
    *d. none of these

41. If the T score equals 51, then the equivalent raw score

    a. must be greater than 100
    b. must be less than 100
    *c. must be greater than the raw score mean
    d. must be greater than the T score mean

42. A raw score which falls exactly at the 5th decile, must convert to a
    T score of

    *a. 50
    b. 100
    c. 0
    d. none of these

43. A raw score which falls exactly at the second quartile, must convert
    to a T score of

    *a. 50
    b. 100
    c. 0
    d. 10

44. On a T score distribution, 68% of the cases must fall between T scores
    of

    a. 50 and 60
    b. 0 and 10
    c. 40 and 50
    *d. 40 and 60

45. Any raw score which has a percentile rank of 99, has a T score of at
    least

    a. 10
    b. 20
    *c. 80
    d. 99

46

46. When T equals 50, then z must equal

    a. 50
    b. 10
  *c. 0
    d. cannot tell from the above information

47. When T equals 50, then the raw score must equal

    a. 50
    b. 10
    c. 0
  *d. cannot tell from the above information

48. When the standard deviation of the raw score distribution is equal to less than 1.00, then

    a. the standard deviation of the T distribution becomes less than 10
    b. the standard deviation of the z distribution becomes less than 10
    c. the standard deviation of the z distribution becomes less than 1
  *d. none of these

49. When converting z to T, all positive z scores yield T scores

  *a. of greater than 50
    b. of greater than 10
    c. of greater than 0
    d. none of these, since z cannot be converted to T

50. The distribution of T scores is assumed to be

    a. Gaussian
    b. normal
    c. mesokurtic
  *d. all of these

B. True or False: For the following, indicate T (True) or F (False)

51. All z scores greater than 0 must coincide with percentiles which are greater than 50.   T

52. All T scores greater than 20 must coincide with percentiles which are greater than 50.   F

53. A person with a T score of greater than 50, must have a negative z score.   F

54. When T=50, then z=0   T

55. The standard deviation of the T distribution must always be greater than 50.   F

56. When the value of the mean is less than the value of the raw score, then the raw score must convert to a T score of greater than 50.   T

57. The standard deviation of the T score distribution is always equal to 10.   T

58. If one knows the mean, the raw score and the z score, then the
    z score equation can be used to calculate the standard deviation. T

59. If a distribution is normal, any percentile can be converted
    into its equivalent z score.   T

60. When the value of T equals 40, the z score must be positive.   F

61. When the z score is negative, so too is the T score.   F

62. For a given raw score to be converted into a z score, one
    must know both the mean and standard deviation of the raw score
    distribution.   T

63. When a T score is greater than 50, so too is its equivalent
    percentile.   T

64. Raw scores may never be converted into T scores unless the raw
    score distribution is normal.   T

65. The range of the T score distribution is approximately 10.   F

66. When a given raw score value is less than the mean of the raw
    score distribution, its equivalent z score must be positive.   F

67. On the T score distribution the standard deviation always
    equals 10.   T

68. If the mean of an IQ distribution equals 100, with a standard
    deviation of 15, then an IQ score of 85 is equivalent to a T
    score of 35.   F

69. All T scores are positive in sign.   T

70. A z score of -1, indicates a point one standard deviation unit
    below the mean.   T

C. For the following questions, calculate the values. Assume normal distribution in all questions.

71. On a test with a mean of 200 and an SD of 50, what raw score would fall
    at the 86th percentile?

    Ans. 254

72. With a mean of 100 and an SD of 20, what raw score would fall at the
    75th percentile?

    Ans. 113.40

73. The mean is 100, with an SD of 15. What raw score would fall at the
    11th percentile?

    Ans. 81.55

74. The mean is 65, with an SD of 5.00. A raw score of 57 would fall at what percentile?

Ans. 5.48, or 5th percentile

75. With a mean of 100 and an SD of 20, what raw score would fall at the 27th percentile?

Ans. 87.80

76. The T score on a certain distribution is 28. The mean of the raw score distribution is 110, with an SD of 14.93. What is the value of the equivalent raw score?

Ans. 77.15

77. The mean on a test is 75 with an SD of 10. What is the raw score for a percentile rank of 80?

Ans. 83.40

78. With a mean of 105 and an SD of 6.30, what raw score falls at the 93rd percentile?

Ans. 114.32

79. The mean is 38.70 with an SD of 6.31. What score falls at the 11th percentile?

Ans. 30.94

80. The mean on a test is 90, with an SD of 20. What raw score would be equivalent to a percentile rank of 29?

Ans. 79.00

81. On a distribution with a mean of 75 and an SD of 15, what raw score falls at the 95th percentile?

Ans. 99.75

82. The mean height for a group of children is normally distributed, with a mean of 55" and an SD of 3.71". One child is at the 39th percentile of the height distribution. How tall is that child?

Ans. 53.96"

83. A certain raw score equals 85 and is at the 15th percentile. The standard deviation is 15.27. What is the mean of the distribution?

Ans. 100.88

84. A certain raw score equals 85 and is at the 85th percentile. The standard deviation is 15.27. What is the mean of the distribution?

Ans. 69.12

85. A certain raw score equals 160 and is at the 53rd percentile. The standard deviation is 10.00. What is the mean of the distribution?

Ans. 159.20

86. A certain raw score equals 71 and is at the 72nd percentile. The standard deviation is 3.00. What is the mean of the distribution?

Ans. 69.26

87. A certain raw score equals 12 and has a percentile rank of 30. The standard deviation is 2.93. What is the mean of the distribution?

Ans. 13.52

88. The mean equals 60. One individual scores at the 13th percentile and has a raw score of 50. What is the standard deviation?

Ans. 8.85

89. With a mean of 55, a raw score of 42 is at the 39th percentile. What is the standard deviation?

Ans. 46.43

90. With a mean of 100, a raw score of 85 is at the 20th percentile. What is the standard deviation?

Ans. 17.86

91. With a mean of 100, a raw score of 107 is at the 58th percentile. What is the standard deviation?

Ans. 35.00

92. With a mean of 30, a raw score of 26 is at the 26th percentile. What is the standard deviation?

Ans. 6.25

For questions 93 through 97, find the T score.

93. $z = 1.28$

Ans. 62.80

94. $z = -.10$

Ans. 49.00

95. $z = 2.58$

Ans. 75.80

96. $z = 1.65$

Ans. 33.50

97. z = 0

    Ans. 50.00

98. With a mean of 150 and an SD of 17, find the T score for a raw score of 180.

    Ans. 67.60

99. With a mean of 68 and an SD of 3.07, find the T score for a raw score of 65.

    Ans. 40.20

100. The T score on a certain distribution is 28. The mean of the raw score distribution is 110 with an SD of 14.93. What is the value of the raw score?

    Ans. 77.15

101. The T score on a certain distribution is 57. The mean of the raw score distribution is 95 with an SD of 10.51. What is the value of the raw score?

    Ans. 102.36

102. With a mean of 15 and an SD of 2.58, find the T score for a raw score of 12.

    Ans. 38.40

103. The T score on a certain distribution is 75. The mean of the raw score distribution is 430 with a SD of 82. What is the value of the raw score?

    Ans. 635.00

104. With a mean of 68, and an SD of 2.95, what is the T score for a raw score of 75?

    Ans. 73.70

105. The T score on a certain distribution is 20. The mean of the raw score distribution is 100 with an SD of 14.97. What is the value of the raw score?

    Ans. 55.09

106. With an SD of 7, a raw score of 55 is at the 23rd percentile. Find the mean.

    Ans. 60.18

A. Multiple Choice Items

1. Probability is defined as

     a. the number of total events over the number of chances
     b. the chances an event cannot occur over the chances it can
    *c. the number of times a specific event will occur over the
         total number of events
     d. the total number of events over the number of times a
         specific event will occur

2. Probability is equal to

    *a. $\dfrac{s}{t}$

     b. $\dfrac{t}{s}$

     c. odds divided by chances
     d. none of these

3. A probability value of .25 means that an event will occur

     a. once out of 25 times
    *b. 25 times out of 100
     c. once out of 5 times
     d. 75 times out of 100

4. If an event can occur once out of 20 times, its probability value is

     a. .20
     b. .80
     c. .95
    *d. .05

5. If an event can occur five times out of 100, its probability value is

     a. .20
     b. .80
     c. .95
    *d. .05

6. Suppose you had flipped a coin 19 times and "heads" had come up each
    time. The probability of flipping a "head" on the 20th flip would
    then be

    *a. .50
     b. .05
     c. .95
     d. .01

7. Suppose you had flipped a coin 19 times and "tails" had come up each
    time. The probability of now tossing a "head" on the 20th flip would
    then be

    *a. .50   c. .95
     b. .05   d. .99

8. When events cannot influence or be influenced by other events, they are said to be

   a. low-probability events
   b. high-probability events
   c. chance events
   *d. independent events

9. The so-called "Gambler's Fallacy" makes the mistake of not recognizing

   a. the low-probability events
   b. the high-probability events
   *c. the independent-events situation
   d. that losses occur more frequently than wins

10. The so-called law of averages only applies

   a. under controlled conditions
   b. when the probabilities are conditional
   *c. in the long run
   d. in the short run

11. If the odds against an event are 5 to 1, the probability of its occurrence is

   *a. .17
   b. .05
   c. .01
   d. .25

12. If the odds against an event are 19 to 1, the probability of its occurrence is

   a. .17
   *b. .05
   c. .01
   d. .25

13. If the odds against an event are 3 to 1, the probability of its occurrence is

   a. .17
   b. .05
   c. .01
   *d. .25

14. Odds are based on how often a given event

   a. will occur out of 100 times
   b. will occur out of any number of times
   c. will occur just once
   *d. will not occur at all, to the number of times it will

15. Probability is based on how often a given event

   *a. will occur out of 100 times
   b. will occur out of 52 times
   c. will occur just once
   d. will not occur at all

16. When the frequency of an event is 25%, its probability is

    a. 3 to 1
    *b. .25
    c. .75
    d. none of these

17. When the frequency of an event is 75%, its probability is

    a. 3 to 1
    b. .25
    c. .67
    *d. none of these

18. The forecaster who believed that flipping coins could predict the
    outcome of elections

    *a. was committing the "Gambler's Fallacy"
    b. was confusing odds with probability
    c. was violating the "Law of Averages"
    d. should have used dice instead of coins

19. If an event has a probability value of .95, its frequency of occurrence
    is

    a. 5%
    *b. 95%
    c. 19 to 1
    d. 47.5%

20. When tossing coins, the frequency of occurrence of "heads" turning up is

    a. .50
    b. .50%
    c. 1 to 1
    *d. 50%

21. When tossing coins, the odds against a "head" turning up are

    a. .50
    b. .50%
    *c. 1 to 1
    d. 2 to 1

22. Under the normal curve, the probability of a score occurring
    within one standard deviation (plus or minus) of the mean is

    *a. .68
    b. .50
    c. 2 to 1
    d. .68%

23. Under the normal curve, the probability of a score occuring
    above the mean is

    a. .68
    *b. .50
    c. 2 to 1
    d. .68%

24. Under the normal curve, the probability of a score occurring below the mean is

    a. .68
*b. .50
    c. 2 to 1
    d. .68%

25. When an event must occur, its probability value is

    a. .99
*b. 1.00
    c. 0
    d. 100%

26. When an event cannot occur, its probability value is

    a. .99
    b. 1.00
*c. 0
    d. 100%

27. The reason z scores may be used to calculate probabilities is that

*a. frequencies are easily converted into probabilities
    b. all z scores are independent of each other
    c. all z scores are included within a standard deviation unit (plus or minus) of the mean
    d. all z scores are included within 2 standard deviation units (plus or minus) of the mean

28. The probability of obtaining a z score of +1.00 or higher, is

    a. 1.00
*b. .16
    c. .84
    d. .34

29. The probability of obtaining a z score of +1.00 or lower, is

    a. 1.00
    b. .16
*c. .84
    d. .34

30. The probability of obtaining a z score of 0 or above is

    a. 0
    b. .16
    c. .34
*d. .50

31. Under the normal curve, the probability of any single score falling below the mean is

    a. 0
    b. .16
    c. .34
*d. .50

32. Under the normal curve, the probability of any single score being above the 50th percentile is

    a. 0
    b. .16
    c. .34
    *d. .50

33. Under the normal curve, the probability of any single score being between z scores of ±3.00, is

    a. 1.00
    b. -1.00
    *c. .99
    d. .50

34. No probability value may ever be greater than

    *a. 1.00
    b. .99
    c. 0
    d. there is no upper limit to the size of a given probability value

35. No probability value may ever be less than

    a. 1.00
    b. .99
    *c. 0
    d. there is no lower limit to the size of a given probability value

36. Under the normal curve, the probability of any score falling below the 50th percentile, is

    a. 0
    b. .16
    c. -.50
    *d. .50

37. Under the normal curve, the middle-most 30% of all scores will be found

    a. between the mean and the 80th percentile
    b. between the mean and the 20th percentile
    c. between the mean and a z of 1.00
    *d. between the 35th and 65th percentiles

38. Under the normal curve, the middle-most 50% of all scores will be found

    a. right at the mean
    *b. within 25%, either side, of the mean
    c. within 50%, either side, of the mean
    d. between the mean and the 100th percentile

39. The middle-most 68% of all z scores fall between z's of

    *a. ±1.00
    b. ±2.00
    c. +1.00 and +2.00
    d. -1.00 and -2.00

56

40. Under the curve, the "middle-most" scores define the

    a. exclusion area
 *b. inclusion area
    c. probability area
    d. entire area under the curve

41. Under the normal curve, the "most extreme" scores define the

 *a. exclusion area
    b. inclusion area
    c. probability area
    d. entire area under the curve

42. Under the normal curve, a probability value of 1.00 defines the

    a. exclusion area
    b. inclusion area
    c. probability area
 *d. entire area under the curve

43. When the "middle-most" area of the curve includes 80% of the cases, then

    a. only the highest 20% are being excluded
    b. only the lowest 20% are being excluded
    c. both the highest 20% and the lowest 20% are being excluded
 *d. both the highest 10% and the lowest 10% are being excluded

44. The "exclusion" area of the curve always contains

    a. the middle-most scores
    b. only the scores at the top of the distribution
    c. only the scores at the bottom of the distribution
 *d. none of these

45. The "most extreme" scores in any distribution are those

    a. occurring above a z of 3.00
    b. occurring below a x of -3.00
    c. occurring at the mean
 *d. occurring furthest from the mean

46. The 68% "inclusion area" falls between

    a. the mean and a z of 1.00
    b. the mean and a z of .68
    c. the mean and the upper tail
 *d. z's of +1.00 and -1.00

47. When the extreme 10% of all scores have been excluded, then the inclusion area contains

    a. 40% of the scores
    b. 80% of the scores
 *c. 90% of the scores
    d. 95% of the scores

48. When the middle-most 60% of all scores have been included, then the exclusion area contains

    a. 30% of the scores
    *b. 40% of the scores
    c. 20% of the scores
    d. 15% of the scores

49. The use of z scores for obtaining probabilities is only possible when

    a. the events are independent
    b. the probabilities are conditional
    c. the distribution curve is symmetrical
    *d. the distribution curve is normal

50. The "inclusion" area always falls

    a. to the right of the mean
    b. under the tails of the curve
    *c. closest to the mean
    d. to the left of the mean

51. A score which is 9 percentage points above the mean, is just within the

    *a. 20% inclusion area
    b. 10% inclusion area
    c. 9% inclusion area
    d. 9% exclusion are

52. A score which is within 4 percentage points from the top of the distribution is just within the

    a. 20% exclusion area
    *b. 10% exclusion area
    c. 5% exclusion area
    d. 5% inclusion area

53. A z score of +1.00, excludes

    a. 68%
    b. 34%
    *c. 32%
    d. 5%

B. <u>True or False</u>: For the following, indicate T (True) or F (False)

54. All probability values lie within the range of +1 to   F
    -1.00.

55. No probability value can ever be greater than 1.00.   T

56. When an event occurs at a frequency of 95%, its   F
    probability value is .05.

57. An event which occurs at a high frequency also has a   T
    high probability of occurring.

58. When the odds against an event occurring are 9 to 1,   T
    the probability that the event will occur is .10.

59. A probability value of 0 indicates that the event can   T
    never occur

60. When a specific event has a probability value of .05,   F
    then its frequency of occurrence is 95%.

61. When an event must occur, its probability is 100.   F

62. The middle-most 10% of the cases in a normal distribution T
    fall in such a way that 5% of these cases lie to the
    right of the mean.

63. On a normal distribution 68% of the cases must fall   F
    above the mean.

64. The ratio, $\frac{s}{t}$, defines probability.   T

65. Probability is always stated in terms of how often an   T
    event will occur.

66. When events are included between two negative z scores   T
    the probability value for those events must be less
    than .50.

67. The probability that any given event may be included   F
    between two positive z scores must be greater than .50.

68. The probability of any event occurring above the mean   F
    is at least .68.

69. The "Gambler's Fallacy" overlooks the fact that   F
    probability values may never be greater than 100.

70. If a coin is flipped 10 times, and by chance, heads   T
    turn up 10 times, on the next flip the probability of
    again obtaining a head is .50.

71. The probability of any event falling within one   T
    standard deviation of the mean (plus or minus) is .68.

72. A negative z score must yield a positive probability value. T

73. Under the normal curve, the exclusion of the most extreme F
    scores refers only to the highest scores in the distribution.

C. For the following questions, calculate the values. Assume a
    normal distribution in all questions.

74. The mean is 55 with an SD of 15. What is the probability of
    selecting at random a score which falls between 60 and 65?

    Ans. .12

75. The mean weight for a group of students is 130 pounds, with an SD of 8
    pounds. What is the probability of selecting a single student who
    weighs 125 pounds or more?

    Ans. .74

59

76. The mean IQ in a certain sorority is 120 with an SD of 5. What is the probability of selecting ar random a student whose IQ is between 130 and 135?

    Ans. .02

77. A certain air-force missile has an average range of 1500 miles with a standard deviation of 62 miles. What is the probability that any single shot will travel 1400 miles or less?

    Ans. .05

78. With a mean of 40 and an SD of 20.45, what is the probability of selecting at random a score of 45 or higher?

    Ans. .41

79. With a mean of 95 and an SD of 12, what is the probability of selecting at random a score of between 89 and 101?

    Ans. .38

80. With a mean of 55 and an SD of 6, what is the probability of selecting at random someone scoring between 48 and 50?

    Ans. .08

81. At a certain race track, the horses run the mile in an average time of 135 seconds, with an SD of 13 seconds. What is the probability of selecting at random a horse which could run the mile in 130 seconds or less?

    Ans. .35

82. With a mean of 70 and an SD of 10, what is the probability of selecting a score of between 75 and 90?

    Ans. .29

83. With a mean of 60 and an SD of 4, what is the probability of selecting at random a score between 56 and 58?

    Ans. .15

84. The average life of a certain light bulb is 200 hours with an SD of 27 hours. What is the probability of selecting at random a bulb lasting 150 hours or less?

    Ans. .03

85. At a certain college, the mean college-board score in math is 400 with an SD of 97. What is the probability of selecting at random a student who scored between 370 and 450?

    Ans. .32

86. With a mean of 75 and an SD of 6.83, find the two raw scores which exclude the extreme 6% of the distribution.

    Ans. 62.16 and 87.84

87. With a mean of 500 and an SD of 93.75, find the two raw scores which exclude the extreme 12% of the distribution.

    Ans. 353.75 and 646.25

88. With a mean of 57.50 and an SD of 7.50, find the two raw scores which exclude the extreme 4% of the distribution.

    Ans. 42.12 and 72.88

89. With a mean of 115 and an SD of 46.15, find the two raw scores which exclude the extreme 18% of the distribution.

    Ans. 53.16 and 176.84

90. With a mean of 30 and an SD of 6.25, find the two raw scores which include the middle-most 80% of the distribution.

    Ans. 22 and 38

91. With a mean of 50 and an SD of 24, find the two raw scores which include the middle-most 20% of the distribution.

    Ans. 44 and 56

92. With a mean of 55 and an SD of 46.43, find the two raw scores which include the middle-most 82% of the distribution.

    Ans. -7.22 and 117.22

93. With a mean of 10 and an SD of 3, find the two raw scores which include the middle-most 90% of the distribution.

    Ans. 5.05 and 14.95

94. With a mean of 100 and an SD of 17.86, find the two raw scores which include the middle-most 95% of the distribution.

    Ans. 64.99 and 135.01

95. The mean is 60 with an SD of 8.85. Find the two raw scores which exclude the extreme 5% of the distribution.

    Ans. 42.65 and 77.35

96. With a mean of 115 and an SD of 46.15, what two raw scores exclude the extreme 18% of the distribution.

    Ans. 53.16 and 176.84

97. With a mean of 100 and an SD of 20.27, find the two raw scores which exclude the extreme 12% of the distribution.

    Ans. 68.38 and 131.62

98. With a mean of 75 and an SD of 10.45, find the two raw scores which include the middle-most 15% of the distribution.

    Ans. 73.01 and 76.99

99. With a mean of 110 and an SD of 13.51, find the two raw scores which include the middle-most 30% of the distribution.

    Ans. 104.73 and 115.27

100. With a mean of 100 and an SD of 17.24, find the two raw scores which exclude the extreme 12% of the distribution.

    Ans. 73.11 and 126.89

101. With a mean of 100 and an SD of 9.52, find the two raw scores which exclude the extreme 16% of the distribution.

    Ans. 86.58 and 113.42

102. With a mean of 100 and an SD of 32.26, find the two raw scores which include the middle-most 90% of the distribution.

    Ans. 46.77 and 153.23

103. With a mean of 45 and an SD of 14.14, find the two raw scores which include the middle-most 85% of the distribution.

    Ans. 24.64 and 65.36

CHAPTER 7
STATISTICS AND PARAMETERS

A. Multiple Choice Items

1. The technique of inferential statistics are designed to yield

   a. eternal truth
   b. data descriptions
   *c. probability estimates
   d. all of these

2. Predicting the characteristics of an entire group, after having measured a small group, is the major goal of

   a. probability theory
   b. descriptive statistics
   c. measurement theory
   *d. inferential statistics

3. An entire group of persons, things or events having at least one trait in common defines the

   *a. population
   b. sample
   c. statistic
   d. measurement scale

4. The size of a given population may be

   a. finite
   b. infinite
   c. determined on the basis of the total number of observations sharing a given trait
   *d. all of these

5. Any value which is based on having measured the entire population is called

   *a. a parameter
   b. a statistic
   c. a finite measure
   d. none of these

6. Populations are to parameters as samples are to

   a. populations
   *b. statistics
   c. infinite measures
   d. finite measures

7. Any value which is based on having measured a sample is called

   a. a parameter
   *b. a statistic
   c. an infinite measure
   d. biased

8. When the population mean differs from the sample mean, the result is called

    a. bias
    b. statistical regression
    c. measurement transformation
  *d. sampling error

9. When a sample mean is greater than the true, population mean, the resulting difference is called

    a. bias
    b. statistical regression
    c. measurement transformation
  *d. sampling error

10. When sample means are consistently lower than the true, population mean, the result is called

  *a. bias
    b. statistical regression
    c. measurement transformation
    d. sampling error

11. If the names of all the students at Omega University were placed in a fishbowl, and the researcher selected out 10% of the names, the resulting sample would be

    a. biased
  *b. random
    c. stratified
    d. far too small for meaningful analysis

12. In order to make accurate population estimates, the sample must be

    a. very large
  *b. representative of the population
    c. manipulated by the experimenter
    d. free of any possible sampling error

13. If the names of all the students at Omega University were dropped into a fishbowl, they would constitute

  *a. the population of Omega students
    b. a sample of Omega students
    c. a random sample of Omega students
    d. all of these, depending on the size of the enrollment at Omega University

14. Random sampling occurs when

    a. the sample is selected from a single population
    b. a random choice determines the first subject to be selected
    c. the sample is selected from an infinite population
  *d. all members of the population have an equal chance of being selected

15. It is assumed that a random sample

    a. must contain bias
    b. is too much a matter of chance to be dependable
    c. is only valid when used for descriptive purposes
  *d. will be representative of the population

16. If Omega University had a total student enrollment of 6000, and 5999 of these students were selected for testing, the group being tested would constitute

  *a. a sample
    b. a population
    c. a parameter
    d. a statistic

17. Omega University has a total student enrollment of 6000, and all 6000 students were tested for IQ. The mean IQ for the group was 115. This value of 115 constitutes a

    a. statistic
    b. population
    c. sample
  *d. parameter

18. If 10 Omega University students were selected out of the total population of 6000, and the median IQ for this small group equaled 118, then this value of 118 would constitute a

  *a. statistic
    b. population
    c. sample
    d. parameter

19. If the mean IQ of all Omega University students was equal to 115, and a small sample of students was selected from the population whose mean IQ was 120, then this difference of 5 points would equal

    a. the parameter
    b. the statistic
  *c. the sampling error
    d. the deviation quartile

20. If every 10th student entering the college library on a Tuesday afternoon were selected for testing, the group thus selected would constitute

  *a. a sample
    b. a random sample
    c. a quota sample
    d. a statistic

21. When a group is selected from a population on the basis of sharing the same percentages of trait characteristics as are known to exist in the population, then the group so selected would constitute

    a. a random sample
  *b. a stratified sample
    c. a biased sample
    d. a sampling distribution

22. When a group is truly selected randomly from a population, the probability of its mean value being higher than the parameter mean is

    a. 0
    *b. .50
    c. 1.00
    d. .33

23. Sampling error is assumed to result

    *a. when any sample is selected
    b. only when a non-representative sample is selected
    c. only when a biased sample is selected
    d. only when the researcher makes a mistake

24. Whenever the sampling error is consistently in <u>one</u> direction, the result is

    a. a negative sampling error
    b. a positive sampling error
    c. a population exclusion
    *d. bias

25. The probability of obtaining a random sample mean which is <u>lower</u> than the population mean is

    a. 1.00
    b. 0
    *c. .50
    d. none of these, since a sample mean can never be lower than a population mean

26. The normal, expected difference between a statistic and a parameter is called

    *a. sampling error
    b. bias
    c. controlled randomization
    d. none of these, since statistics and parameters may never differ

27. The reason the Literary Digest's 1936 election poll was so inaccurate, was that

    a. the sample was too small
    b. it contained sampling error
    *c. the sample was biased
    d. the wrong statistical tests were employed for extrapolating to the population

28. Any sample which contains fewer than 50% of the total population

    a. must be biased
    b. must be non-random
    c. must be inaccurate
    *d. none of these

29. The sample selected by the Literary Digest in 1936 was

    a. far too small to be accurate
  *b. overly represented by affluent voters
    c. overly represented by Democrats
    d. truly random

30. The problem with the Gallup poll of 1948 (when Dewey was predicted to beat Truman) was that

    a. the polling ended too soon
    b. the "undecideds" were split 50/50
    c. many of the "undecideds" had, in fact, already made up their minds
  *d. all of these

31. The sum total of all registered voters in Canada represents

  *a. the population of potential Canadian voters
    b. a parameter
    c. a statistic
    d. sampling error

32. A biased sample can <u>never</u> be

    a. selected from a single population
    b. selected when the parameters are known
    c. selected when the entire population is available
  *d. representative of the population

33. By definition, one can never obtain a statistic unless

    a. the entire population has been measured
    b. a random sample has been measured
    c. a quota sample has been measured
  *d. none of these, since a statistic refers to a measure of any type of sample

34. When graphing the sampling distribution of means, the ordinate represents

    a. a sample mean
    b. a population mean
    c. a statistical mean
  *d. the frequency of occurrence

35. When graphing the sampling distribution of means, the various sample means are represented on

  *a. the abscissa
    b. the ordinate
    c. the Y axis
    d. none of these

36. Each point on the abscissa of the distribution of sample means represents

    a. a parameter
    *b. a statistic
    c. the sampling error
    d. the population error

37. The mean of the entire distribution of sample means represents

    *a. a parameter
    b. a statistic
    c. the sampling error
    d. none of these

38. The sampling distribution of means assumes normality only when

    a. all samples are randomly selected
    b. all samples have been selected from a single population
    c. the samples represent groups of sufficient size
    *d. all of these

39. The Central Limit theorem states that the sampling distribution of means is

    a. only available by inference
    b. only available when sample sizes are less than 10
    c. only available when the very high and very low means have been eliminated
    *d. normal in shape

40. The range of values for the sampling distribution of means

    a. is larger than the range of the underlying individual scores
    b. is identical to the range of the underlying individual scores
    *c. is smaller than the range of the underlying individual scores
    d. is always equal to 30 or higher

41. When the sampling distribution of means is randomly selected from an entire population of individual scores, the highest and lowest individual scores

    *a. become lost through averaging
    b. must be arbitrarily eliminated before the sampling distribution becomes available
    c. assume the characteristics of parameters
    d. produce a bimodal distribution

42. When the standard deviation of the entire distribution of random sample means has been calculated, the resulting value is called

    a. the deviation score
    b. the parameter mean
    *c. the standard error of the mean
    d. sampling error

43. The probability estimates provided by inferential statistics are only necessary when

    *a. the population values are unknown
    b. the parameters are given
    c. the population values are provided
    d. none of these

44. When comparing the size of the standard error of the mean with the size of the standard deviation of the underlying distribution of individual scores,

    a. the standard error of the mean is always larger
    *b. the standard error of the mean is always smaller
    c. the standard error of the mean is sometimes larger and sometimes smaller, depending on the sample size
    d. none of these

45. The fact that the distribution of random sample means is assumed to be normal is expressed in

    a. the Gaussian Law
    b. Pascal's triangle
    *c. the Central Limit theorem
    d. none of these, since the premise is false

46. In order to calculate the z test, one must know

    a. the sample's true standard deviation
    b. the amount of sampling error present
    *c. the parameter mean, the parameter standard deviation and the sample mean
    d. the exact amount of bias contained in the sample

47. The z test may be used to determine

    *a. if the sample is representative of a known population
    b. if a sample contains bias
    c. the exact amount of sampling error contained in the parameter mean
    d. the amount of sampling error contained in the population's standard deviation

48. The z test assumes that

    a. the sample mean is equal to the population mean
    b. the standard deviation of the sample scores is equal to the standard deviation of the distribution of sample means
    *c. the distribution of sample means is normal
    d. none of these, since the z test is "assumption free"

49. The standard error of the mean must equal

    a. the standard deviation of the sample's distribution of individual scores
    b. the standard deviation of the entire population's distribution of individual scores
    c. the "average" of the sample's distribution of individual scores and the population's distribution of individual scores
    *d. the standard deviation of the entire sampling distribution of means

50. When all possible samples have been randomly selected from a single population, the standard deviation of the resulting distribution of means is called

    a. the "true" standard deviation of the sample's individual scores
    b. the "true" standard deviation of the population's individual scores
 *c. the standard error of the mean
    d. sample variance plus error variance

51. One measure of the overall sampling error in the entire distribution of sample means is the

 *a. standard error of the mean
    b. population mean
    c. population median
    d. sample's true amount of bias

B. <u>True or False</u>: For the following, indicate T (True) or F (False)

52. A population may never share more than one common trait.   F

53. A statistic always refers to a sample measure.   T

54. Statistic is to sample as parameter is to population.   T

55. True populations may never be infinite.   F

56. Bias is the difference between the sample measure and the population measure.   F

57. With true random sampling, every observation in the population has an equal chance of being selected.   T

58. When sampling error is constant and in one direction, the sampling must be biased.   T

59. The major error in inferential statistics is to commit the "sampling error".   F

60. Each and every time a sample is selected, sampling error must be assumed.   T

61. The Central Limit theorem states the probability value of estimating the true mean.   F

62. The Central Limit theorem states that the sampling distribution of means is normal in shape.   T

63. Stratified sampling refers to the actual number of different samples being selected from a single population.   F

64. When samples are selected randomly, they are assumed to be representative of the population.   T

65. The z test assumes that the sampling distribution of means is normal.   T

66. For the z test, the null hypothesis states that the sample
    and parameter means are equal.   T

67. The z test assumes that the sample's standard deviation equals
    the standard error of the mean.   F

68. The z test assumes knowledge of the two population parameters,
    the mean and the standard deviation.   T

69. The Central Limit theorem only applies when the distribution of
    individual sample scores is normal.   F

70. The null hypothesis for the z test, since it is based on chance,
    must always be accepted.   F

71. The z test draws a comparison between the sample mean and the
    known population mean.   T

C. For the following questions, calculate the values.

72. With a known population mean of 100, and a known standard error of the
    mean of 7.5, what is the probability of selecting at random a sample
    whose mean is equal to 110 or greater?

    Ans. p=.09

73. With a known population mean of 1500, and a known standard error of the
    mean of 42.50, what is the probability of selecting at random a sample
    whose mean is 1450 of less?

    Ans. p=.12

74. With a known population mean of 10 and a known standard error of the
    mean of 1.47, what is the probability of selecting at random a sample
    whose mean is 8.50 or less?

    Ans. p=.15

75. With a known population mean of 68 and a known standard error of the
    mean of 2.58, what is the probability of selecting at random a sample
    whose mean is 70 or greater?

    Ans. p=.22

76. With a known population mean of 50 and a known standard error of the
    mean of 4.00, what is the probability of selecting at random a sample
    whose mean is 52 or greater?

    Ans. p=.31

77. With a known population mean of 75 and a known standard error of the
    mean of 5.00, what is the probability of selecting at random a sample
    whose mean is 70 or less?

    Ans. p=.16

78. The standard deviation of the population of individual scores is 22.50. A given random sample of 100 scores produces a mean of 210. Calculate the standard error of the mean.

   Ans. 2.25

79. The standard deviation of the population of individual scores is 15. A random sample of 10 scores yields a mean of 100. Calculate the standard error of the mean.

   Ans. 4.75

80. The standard deviation in the population of individual verbal SAT scores is 100. A random sample of 45 subjects yields a mean score of 500. Calculate the standard error of the mean.

   Ans. 14.90

81. The standard deviation of the population of adult female height scores is 3 inches. A random sample of 50 women yields a mean height of 64 inches. Calculate the standard error of the mean.

   Ans. .42

82. The standard deviation of the population of individual adult male weight scores is 25 pounds. A random sample of 70 adult males produces a mean of 180 pounds.
   a. Calculate the standard error of the mean.
   b. Test the hypothesis, via the z test, that this sample could still be representative of a population whose mean is known to be 170 pounds.

   Ans. a. 2.91
         b. $z = 3.45$. Reject the null hypothesis at P .01. The sample probably does not represent the population at large.

83. The standard deviation of the population of individual scores is 15. A random sample of 40 subjects yields a mean of 105.
   a. Calculate the standard error of the mean.
   b. Test the hypothesis, via the z test, that this sample could be representative of a population whose mean is known to be 100.

   Ans. a. 2.37
         b. $z = 2.11$. Reject the null hypothesis at P .05. The sample probably does not represent the population at large.

84. The standard deviation of the population of individual scores is 2.50. A random sample of 100 subjects yields a mean of 70.
   a. Calculate the standard error of the mean.
   b. Test the hypothesis, via the z test, that this sample could be representative of a population whose mean is known to be 76.

   Ans. a. .25
         b. $z = -24.00$. Reject the null hypothesis at P .01. The sample probably does not represent the population at large.

85. The standard deviation of the population of individual Digit Span scores
    is 3.00. (The Digit Span test is a sub-test of the Wechsler IQ test).
    A random sample of 20 subjects yielded a mean Digit Span score of 7.25.
    a. Calculate the standard error of the mean.
    b. Test the hypothesis, using the z test, that the sample could be
       representative of a population whose mean is known to be 10.00.

    Ans. a. .67
          b. $z = -4.10$. Reject null hypothesis at P .01. The sample
             probably does not represent the population at large.

86. The standard deviation of the population of individually measured adult
    male spine lengths is 1.02 inches. A random sample of 25 men is selected
    and the mean spine length was recorded at 30 inches.
    a. Calculate the standard error of the mean.
    b. Test the hypothesis that this sample could be representative of the
       general population of adult males whose mean spine length is known
       to be 28 inches.

    Ans. a. .20
          b. $z = 10.00$. Reject null hypothesis at P .01. The sample
             probably does not represent the population at large.

87. The standard deviation of the population of adult female spine lengths
    is .92 inches. A random sample of 40 women was selected and the mean
    spine length was found to be 26 inches.
    a. Calculate the standard error of the mean.
    b. Use the z test to establish whether this sample could be representa-
       tive of the general population of women whose mean spine length is
       known to be 24 inches.

    Ans. a. .15
          b. $z = 13.33$. Reject null hypothesis at P .01. The sample
             probably does not represent the population at large.

88. The standard deviation of the population of elementary school math-
    achievement scores is 7.78. A random sample of 20 elementary school
    children was selected and yielded a mean achievement score of 80.04.
    a. Calculate the standard error of the mean.
    b. Use the z test to establish whether this sample could be
       representative of the general population of elementary school
       children whose mean math achievement score is known to be 78.00.

    Ans. a. 1.74
          b. $z = 1.17$. Accept null hypothesis. The sample probably
             does represent the population at large.

89. The standard deviation of the population of men's collar sizes is 1.02
    inches. A random sample of 12 men was selected and yielded a mean
    collar size of 15.50 inches.
    a. Calculate the standard error of the mean.
    b. Use the z test to establish whether this sample could
       represent the population of men's collar sizes which is known
       to have a mean of 15 inches.

    Ans. a. .29
          b. $z = 1.72$. Accept the null hypothesis. The sample probably
             does represent the population at large.

A. Multiple Choice

1. With a small-sized sample the estimated standard deviation of the
   population yields a value which is

   *a. smaller than the true standard deviation of the sample
   b. the same as the true standard deviation of the sample
   c. larger than the true standard deviation of the sample
   d. none of these, since the population standard deviation may never
   be estimated

2. The estimated standard deviation of the population always yields

   *a. a statistic
   b. a parameter
   c. a measure of central tendency
   d. none of these

3. The reason that the true standard deviation of the sample is called
   a "biased estimator" is because with small samples

   a. it over-estimates the population standard deviation
   *b. it under-estimates the population standard deviation
   c. it over-estimates just as often as it under-estimates the population
   standard deviation
   d. none of these, since the true standard deviation of the sample can
   never be biased

4. The only way to be absolutely certain that the sample mean will be
   identical with the population mean is to

   a. select the sample randomly
   b. select the sample on a "quota" basis
   c. select a sample which is at least half the size of the population
   *d. none of these

5. The values of the true standard deviation of the sample and the
   estimated standard deviation of the population become increasingly
   similar when

   *a. the sample size increases
   b. the sample size decreases
   c. the sample has a large amount of variability
   d. the sample has a small amount of variability

6. As sample sizes increase,

   a. degrees of freedom decrease
   b. sampling error is eliminated
   c. bias increases
   *d. the values of the true standard deviation of the sample and the
   estimated standard deviation of the population become increasingly
   similar

7. Estimating the value of the population mean on the basis of the sample mean alone produces a(n)

    a. parameter
*b. point estimate of a parameter
    c. estimated statistic
    d. none of these, since the population mean cannot be estimated

8. The fact that the point estimate of the population mean may be inaccurate is due largely to

    a. bias
    b. alpha error
*c. sampling error
    d. none of these, since the population mean cannot be estimated

9. Whenever a sample is selected and measured, one must assume that the sample mean

*a. will probably differ from the population mean
    b. will probably be identical with the population mean
    c. will over-estimate the population mean
    d. will under-estimate the population mean

10. A point estimate of a population value is referred to as

    a. a biases estimator
    b. a true parameter
    c. a true variability measure
*d. an hypothesized parameter

11. According to the text, the highest value that should be assigned to the alpha error is

    a. .95
    b. .99
    c. .10
*d. .05

12. Other things being equal, an alpha error of .05 should lead to a rejection of the null hypothesis

*a. more often than when alpha is set at .01
    b. more often than when alpha is set at .10
    c. less often than when alpha is set at .01
    d. none of these, since when alpha is set at .05, the null hypothesis cannot be rejected

13. If it is determined that there is no difference between the population mean being represented by the sample and the assumed mean of the population at large, then

    a. the alpha error must have been accepted
    b. the alpha error must have been rejected
    c. the alpha error must have been committed
*d. the null hypothesis must have been accepted

14. When a given difference is determined to be "significant", then

    a. the alpha error must have been accepted
    b. the alpha error must have been rejected
    *c. the null hypothesis must have been rejected
    d. the null hypothesis must have been accepted

15. When the null hypothesis is rejected, then we know for certain that

    a. the mean of the sample equals the mean of the population
    b. the mean of the sample differs from the mean of the population
    c. the mean of the sample is a biased estimator
    *d. none of these, since the statistical decision is a probability
        statement and not a statement of certainty

16. When the null hypothesis is accepted, then we know for certain that

    a. the mean of the sample equals the mean of the population
    b. the mean of the sample differs from the mean of the population
    c. the mean of the sample is a biased estimator
    *d. none of these, since the statistical decision is a probability
        statement and not a statement of certainty

17. When an area (between high and low values) of the sampling distribution
    of means has been bracketed on the basis of a reasonable expectation of
    containing the population mean, then

    a. the central limit theorem has been proven
    b. the point estimate has been proven
    c. the alpha level has been calculated
    *d. the confidence interval has been calculated

18. The true population mean is expected to fall outside a .99 confidence
    interval

    *a. 1% of the time
    b. 99% of the time
    c. 100% of the time
    d. none of these, since the true mean may never fall outside the
        confidence interval

19. Increasing the confidence-interval level from .95 to .99

    *a. increases the likelihood of including the population mean within its
        limits
    b. decreases the likelihood of including the population mean within its
        limits
    c. increases the number of degrees of freedom
    d. none of these, since a confidence interval may never include the
        true population mean

20. The single-sample t ratio is used to compare

    a. two population means
    *b. a sample mean with an assumed population mean
    c. two sample means
    d. a single sample's mean with that same sample's standard deviation

21. With a single-sample t ratio, the null hypothesis states that

   *a. the sample mean could readily be part of the same distribution whose overall mean is being hypothesized
   b. the sample mean in all likelihood could not be part of the same distribution whose overall mean was being hypothesized
   c. the sample mean and the population mean are significantly different values
   d. none of these, since the null hypothesis always assumes that at least two sample means have been obtained

22. A single-sample t ratio presents the difference between two means in units of

   *a. the estimated standard error of the mean
   b. the estimated population standard deviation of the underlying distribution of individual scores
   c. the estimated standard error of difference
   d. none of these, since the single-sample t ratio cannot compare two means

23. A single-sample t ratio is only significant when

   a. the population values are known
   b. the population values are assumed
   c. its value falls within the confidence interval
   *d. the null hypothesis has been rejected

24. Other things being equal, the higher the value of the t ratio

   *a. the greater the likelihood of rejecting Ho
   b. the less the likelihood of rejecting Ho
   c. the more certain that the samples represent a single population
   d. the greater the likelihood of sampling error

25. Rejecting Ho when in fact it should have been accepted, causes the

   a. standard error
   b. sampling error
   c. omega error
   *d. alpha error

26. For the t ratio, the larger the sample size

   a. the larger the alpha error
   b. the larger the beta error
   c. the larger the number of groups being compared
   *d. the larger the number of degrees of freedom

27. The alpha error states the probability of being wrong whenever

   a. Ho is accepted
   *b. Ho is rejected
   c. Ho is tested
   d. the sample means are assumed to be equal

28. For the t ratio, the larger the difference between the sample mean and the population mean (other things being equal), the greater the likelihood of

   *a. rejecting Ho
   b.   accepting Ho
   c.   sampling error
   d.   committing the standard error

29. When alpha is set at .05, and Ho is rejected, then the probability is

   *a. .05 that Ho should have been accepted
   b.   .95 that Ho should have been accepted
   c.   .05 that Ho should have been rejected
   d.   .95 that Ho should have been rejected

30. Whenever Ho is <u>rejected</u>, then

   *a. it is possible to commit the alpha error
   b.   it is impossible to commit the alpha error
   c.   the only possible error is sampling error
   d.   none of these

31. For the t test, other things being equal, the smaller the value of the alpha error

   *a. the less likely it becomes to reject Ho
   b.   the more likely it becomes to reject Ho
   c.   the less likely it becomes to accept Ho
   d.   the fewer the degrees of freedom

32. The relationship between the value of the alpha error and the number of degrees of freedom, is that

   a.   the greater the alpha error, the greater the degrees of freedom
   b.   the smaller the alpha error, the greater the degrees of freedom
   c.   degrees of freedom and alpha error take on the same value
   *d. none of these, since alpha error and degrees of freedom are unrelated

33. Whenever the calculated value of t is equal to or greater than the tabled value of t, for a given number of degrees of freedom, then

   a.   Ho is accepted
   *b. Ho is rejected
   c.   Ho is no longer relevant
   d.   the alpha error becomes zero

34. Whenever the calculated value of t is <u>less than</u> the tabled value of t (for a given number of degrees of freedom), then

   *a. Ho is accepted
   b.   Ho is rejected
   c.   Ho is no longer relevant
   d.   the alpha error increases

35. The relationship between the alpha error and the confidence level is such that

*a. the lower the alpha, the higher the confidence level
b. the lower the alpha, the lower the confidence level
c. they are not related until the confidence level reaches .95
d. none of these, since they are not related at all

36. In order to reach a confidence level of .95, then the alpha error must be set at

*a. .05
b. .95
c. .99
d. none of these

37. If a researcher were to conduct 100 experiments, and in each case the null hypothesis were rejected at an alpha of .05, then

*a. chances are that 5% of the decisions were incorrect
b. chances are that 95% of the decisions were incorrect
c. chances are that less than 5% of the decisions were correct
d. none of these, since null can never be rejected 100 times in a row

38. The estimated standard error of the mean can be calculated on the basis of the information

a. provided by a single, individual score
*b. provided in a single sample
c. provided by comparing two sample means
d. provided by comparing a pair of parameters

39. In order to calculate the estimated standard error of the mean, one need only know

*a. the sample's standard deviation and the size of the sample
b. the sample mean
c. the parameter mean
d. the standard deviation of the distribution of individual scores

40. The estimated standard error of the mean is

a. an estimate of the sampling error
b. a parameter
*c. a statistic
d. equal to the range of individual scores, divided by 6

41. The estimated standard error of the mean is equal to

a. the standard deviation of the sample
*b. the standard deviation of the sample, divided by the square-root of the size of the sample, less one
c. the standard deviation of the population multiplied by the size of the population
d. the difference between the mean of the sample and the mean of the population

42. The estimated standard error of the mean takes on a negative value only when

    a. most of the samples are below the mean
    b. populations of less than an N of 30 are involved
    c. populations of more than an N of 30 are involved
    *d. none of these

43. The estimated standard error of the mean is always used to predict

    a. sample size
    b. bias
    c. central tendency
    *d. the variability of the distribution of sample means

44. When estimating the population mean on the basis of the information contained in a single sample, one must at least know

    *a. the estimated standard error of the mean and the mean and size of sample
    b. the z score for each raw score
    c. the standard deviation of the underlying distribution of individual scores
    d. the interdecile range

45. Multiplying the estimated standard error of the mean by 6 yields an approximation of

    a. the range of the entire distribution of individual scores
    *b. the range of the entire sampling distribution of means
    c. the standard deviation of the sample
    d. the standard deviation of the population

46. The estimated standard error of the mean becomes a better predictor whenever the distribution of sample means

    a. is skewed
    b. is bimodal
    c. is platykurtic
    *d. none of these

47. The estimated standard error of the mean is to the standard deviation of the entire distribution of all possible sample means as

    *a. a statistic is to a parameter
    b. a parameter is to a statistic
    c. a parameter is to an estimate
    d. a deviation score is to a raw score

48. The term "confidence" expresses the probability that one's estimate is

    *a. accurate
    b. not accurate
    c. inferred from a population
    d. based on a sample mean

49. The higher the probability value of the confidence interval

    *a. the broader becomes the range of predicted mean values
    b. the more narrow becomes the range of predicted mean values
    c. the less the sampling error
    d. the greater the sampling error

50. When the parameter mean is predicted to lie within a certain range
    of mean values, the technique employed is called

    a. point estimation
    b. error estimation
    *c. interval estimation
    d. inferential validity

51. When the parameter mean is predicted as a single value, the
    technique employed is called

    *a. point estimation
    b. error estimation
    c. interval estimation
    d. inferential validity

52. When the confidence interval has a probability value of .99, then

    a. the resulting prediction is never wrong
    b. the resulting prediction is wrong 99% of the time
    *c. 99% of the resulting predictions are assumed to lie within the
        interval
    d. none of these, since the confidence interval has nothing to do
       with accuracy

53. For the t ratio, other things being equal, having 1 degree of freedom
    rather than 12 degrees of freedom makes it

    a. more likely to reject Ho
    *b. less likely to reject Ho
    c. impossible to reject Ho
    d. none of these

54. The alpha error may never be committed when

    a. Ho is rejected
    *b. Ho is accepted
    c. the direction of Ha is specified
    d. none of these, since there is always some possibility of committing
       the alpha error

B. True or False: For the following, indicate T (True) or F (False)

55. The true mean of the population must always be a known value   F
    before inferential techniques may be employed.

56. The standard error of the mean may never be negative.   T

57. A confidence interval of .99 predicts a narrower range of   F
    mean values than does an interval of .95.

58. A point estimate predicts a single parameter-mean value.   T

59. The techniques of inferential statistics are based on a   T
    probability model, and may sometimes lead to inaccurate
    predictions.

60. The estimated standard error of the mean can only be calculated
    when the entire population of individual scores are available. F

61. The estimated standard error of the mean may be calculated   T
    on the basis of the information contained in a <u>single</u> random
    sample.

62. The alpha error specifies the probability of being correct   F
    when rejecting null.

63. Other things being equal, the fewer the degrees of freedom,   F
    the easier it is to obtain a significant t ratio.

64. With very small sample sizes, the estimated standard   T
    deviation of the population yields a slightly higher value
    than does the true standard deviation of the sample.

65. Because of sampling error, the point estimate of the   T
    population mean may produce an inaccurate prediction.

66. The true standard deviation of the sample may be used directly F
    to estimate the point value of the population mean.

67. The actual mean of the set of sample scores may be used   T
    directly to estimate the point value of the population mean.

68. When subjects are selected randomly, then the larger the sample T
    size, the higher the likelihood of the sample mean approaching
    the population mean.

69. The true standard deviation of the entire distribution of   T
    random sample means is defined as the standard error of the
    mean.

70. The concept of the standard error of the mean indicates that   F
    the actual population mean can never be a true parameter.

71. The concept of the standard error of the mean implies that   F
    the estimated population standard deviation must yield a
    value which over-estimates the true mean.

72. Regardless of sample size, the degrees of freedom assigned   F
    to the single-sample t ratio must remain constant.

73. The only t ratios which can possibly lead to a reject of the   F
    null hypothesis are those which are positive in sign.

74. Negative t ratios may sometimes lead to significant results.   T

75. With a sample size of 30, the single-sample t ratio has   F
    1 degree of freedom.

76. Parameter estimates are considered to be hypotheses.   T

77. A significant difference is one that is probably <u>not</u> due to chance.   T

78. When the null hypothesis is accepted, one must conclude that the difference between the sample mean and the population mean is probably <u>not</u> due to chance.   F

79. The alpha error is typically set at either .95 or .99.   F

80. The alpha error is committed when the null hypothesis is accepted when in fact it should have been rejected.   F

81. Interval estimates, unlike point estimates, are used to predict a single parameter value.   F

82. Other things being equal, increasing the sample size, decreases the width of the confidence interval.   T

83. Other things being equal, the smaller the value of the estimated standard error of the mean, the narrower the confidence interval becomes.   T

84. Other things being equal, a .99 confidence interval produces a wider interval than when the confidence level is set at .95.   T

85. With infinite degrees of freedom, the t distribution approaches normality.   T

86. With extremely large sample sizes, the difference in values between the estimated population standard deviation and the true standard deviation of the sample become minimal.   T

87. The smaller the standard deviation of the sample, for a given N, the larger is the estimated standard error of the mean.   F

88. For a given value for the sample's standard deviation, increasing the sample size increases the value of the standard error of the mean.   F

89. Because of sampling error, the point estimate of the population mean can never provide the "best" estimate of a single parameter value.   F

90. Sampling error always produces bias.   F

91. Random sampling helps to reduce bias.   T

92. True random sampling can be guaranteed to eliminate sampling error.   F

93. The single-sample t ratio may be used to compare the sample mean with an assumed population mean.   T

94. The single-sample t ratio may be used when all the parameter values are known rather than assumed.   F

C. For the following questions, calculate the values

95. For the following set of sample scores, find the estimated standard error of the mean: 25, 21, 17, 16, 15, 14, 11, 8, 7.

    Ans. 1.94

96. For the following set of sample scores, find the estimated standard error of the mean: 15, 14, 14, 13, 12, 12, 12, 11, 10, 9, 9.

    Ans. .61

97. For the following set of sample scores, find the estimated standard error of the mean: 16, 10, 8, 6, 5, 3, 1, 1.

    Ans. 1.79

98. For the following set of sample scores, find the estimated standard error of the mean: 60, 55, 53, 52, 50, 50, 47, 47, 44, 40.

    Ans. 1.80

99. For the following set of sample scores, find the estimated standard error of the mean: 20, 14, 16, 18, 9, 16, 18, 16, 15, 14.

    Ans. .95

100. For the following set of sample scores, find the estimated standard error of the mean: 23, 20, 21, 24, 18, 22, 24, 22, 20, 20.

    Ans. .62

101. For the following set of sample scores, find the estimated standard error of the mean: 12, 11, 9, 4, 8, 2.

    Ans. 1.60

102. For the following set of sample scores, find the estimated standard error of the mean: 4, 3, 2, 2.

    Ans. .96

103. For the following set of sample scores, find the estimated standard error of the mean: 8, 6, 7, 7, 3, 1, 8.

    Ans. 1.02

104. For the following set of sample scores, find the estimated standard error of the mean: 2, 1, 2, 3, 8, 5, 1.

    Ans. .96

105. For the following set of sample scores, estimate the population mean within a .95 confidence interval: 3, 6, 5, 3, 3, 7, 7, 5, 6.

    Ans. From 3.73 to 6.27

106. For the following set of sample scores, estimate the population mean within a .95 confidence interval: 15, 18, 12, 17, 19.

   Ans. From 12.75 to 19.65

107. For the following set of sample scores, estimate the population mean within a .99 confidence interval: 10, 10, 12, 11, 10.

   Ans. From 8.76 to 12.44

108. For the following set of sample scores, estimate the population mean within a .99 confidence interval: 50, 45, 45, 40, 40, 40, 35, 35, 30.

   Ans. From 33.15 to 46.85

For questions 109 through 112, use the following:

   A researcher is interested in evaluating a certain brand of radial auto tire. Twenty tires are randomly selected from retail outlets throughout the country, and each is placed on a special machine which rotates the tires at a constant speed (equivalent to 55 miles per hour) against the friction equivalent of a 4000 pound auto being driven on a smooth highway Each tire is run until there is no tread left. The number of miles (in thousands) were as follows: 40, 30, 32, 35, 39, 35, 31, 36, 37, 35, 34, 35, 37, 34, 36, 38, 35, 36, 35, 36.

109. Find the mean mileage for this sample.

   Ans. 35.30

110. Find the estimated standard error of the mean.

   Ans. 0.54

111. Estimate the population mean within a confidence interval of .95.

   Ans. From 34.17 to 36.43

112. Estimate the population mean within a confidence interval of .99.

   Ans. From 33.76 to 36.84

113. A random sample of 30 infants (age 12 months) was selected and given a Motoric Development test. The mean score for the sample was at the 13.20 month level. The estimated standard error of the mean was 1.25. Estimate whether the mean test age of the sample could be representative of a population whose hypothesized mean test age is 12 months.

   Ans. t=.96 Accept Ho. Difference is not significant.

114. A random sample of 61 fifth-grade students was selected and given the Stanford-Binet IQ test. The mean score for the sample was 97, with an estimated standard error of the mean of 2.43. Estimate whether the sample mean could be representative of the hypothesized population mean of 100.

   Ans. t= -1.23 Accept Ho. Difference is not significant.

115. A random sample of 20 fourth-grade students was selected and given the math sub-test of the Peabody Individual Achievement Test (PIAT). The sample mean was found to be 38.07 with an estimated standard error of the mean of 2.11. The population mean was found to be 42.50. Test whether the sample could be representative of the population.
Ans. t= -2.10 Reject Ho. Difference is significant at p <.05.
Sample is probably not representative of the population.

116. A random sample of 41 children (all 5 years of age) was selected and given the Reading test of the WRAT (Wide Range Achievement Test). The sample mean was 20.57 and the estimated standard error of the mean was 1.98. Test whether the sample could be representative of a population whose hypothesized mean was 23.52.

Ans. t= -1.49 Accept Ho. Difference not significant.

117. A random sample of 10 adult subjects was selected and tested on the Vocabulary sub-test of the Wechsler Adult Intelligence Scale (WAIS). Their scores were as follows: 12,11,10,10,10,7,6,6,5,5. Test whether this sample could be representative of a population whose mean is assumed to be 10.00.

Ans. t= -2.14 Accept Ho. Difference not significant.

118. A random sample of 7 college sophomores was selected and tested for their attitudes toward gun control (high scores indicating a pro attitude and low scores an anti attitude). Their scores were 20,18,15,11,11,8,4. Test whether this sample is representative of a population whose mean is assumed to be 18.00, a value which presumes neutrality.

Ans. t= -2.63 Reject Ho. Difference is significant at p < 05.
Sample is probably not representative of the population.

CHAPTER 9
THE HYPOTHESIS OF DIFFERENCE

A. Multiple Choice Items

1. The distribution of differences is composed of the differences between

   a. raw scores and the mean
   b. the highest and lowest scores in a distribution
   c. the standard deviation and the standard error of the mean
   *d. pairs of randomly selected sample means

2. When graphing the distribution of differences, the abscissa is used to represent

   a. a sample mean
   b. the difference between the mean of the individual raw scores and the sample mean
   *c. the difference between two sample means
   d. the frequency of occurrence

3. When graphing the distribution of differences, the ordinate is used to represent

   a. a sample mean
   b. the difference between the mean of the individual raw scores and the sample mean
   c. the difference between two sample means
   *d. frequency of occurrence

4. When the differences between pairs of randomly selected means are obtained, the resulting distribution is called

   a. the distribution of means
   *b. the distribution of differences
   c. the distribution of individual sample scores
   d. the ogive distribution

5. When all samples are drawn from a single population, the mean of the distribution of differences should approximate

   *a. zero
   b. +1.0
   c. -1.0
   d. the mean of the distribution of means

6. If the mean of the distribution of differences were to equal -6.00, this would indicate that

   a. the standard deviation of the distribution is a function of the range
   *b. the samples were probably selected from different populations
   c. the samples were probably selected from a single population
   d. none of these, since the mean can never be negative

7. Whenever the mean of the distribution of differences equals zero, then
    it can be concluded that

    *a. the samples probably represent a single population
    b.   the samples probably represent different populations
    c.   there was absolutely no sampling error
    d.   none of these, since the mean can never equal zero

8. The estimated standard deviation of the distribution of differences is
    called

    a.   the estimated standard error of the mean
    *b. the estimated standard error of the difference
    c.   the standard error of the estimate
    d.   a standard score

9. If all the possible pairs of sample means were obtained from a single
    population, the mean of the distribution of differences would be

    a.   a statistic
    *b. a parameter
    c.   identical with the mean of the distribution of means
    d.   equal to one-sixth of the range

10. The estimated standard error of difference may be obtained on the basis
    of the information contained in

    a.   a single sample
    *b. a pair of random samples
    c.   the sampling error
    d.   a single z score

11. The estimated standard error of difference is an estimate of

    a.   centrality
    *b. variability
    c.   normality
    d.   none of these, since the estimated standard error of difference is
         not a statistic.

12. The Central Limit theorem states that the distribution of differences is

    a.   based on a single pair of samples
    b.   based on a single sample
    c.   a parameter
    *d. normal in shape

13. When selecting a pair of random-sample means from a single population,
    the probability of the first mean being higher than the second mean is

    a.   1.00
    b.   0
    *c. .50
    d.   either a or b, but never c

14. The distribution of differences is

   *a. a sampling distribution
   b. a distribution of parameters
   c. always leptokurtic in shape
   d. always platykurtic in shape

15. Regarding the distribution of differences, the assumption of normality
   is based on

   a. Pascal's triangle
   b. Gossett's law
   *c. the Central Limit theorem
   d. the Gaussian law

16. When pairs of samples are selected from two separate populations, the
   mean of the distribution of differences is assumed to be

   *a. some value other than zero
   b. zero
   c. a constant
   d. equal to the mean of the distribution of means

17. In order to use the estimated standard error of difference for making
   probability estimates, both samples must

   a. have equal means
   b. have unequal means
   c. be free of sampling error
   *d. have similar amounts of variability

18. In order to ensure a sampling error of zero, each sample must

   a. be randomly selected
   b. be equal in size
   c. be selected from the same population
   *d. none of these, since one can never assume a sampling error of zero

19. Whenever the distribution of differences is normally shaped, and all its
   assumptions are met, then

   a. the samples must represent different populations
   b. the samples must represent a single population
   c. more than two populations must be involved
   *d. none of these, since when its assumptions are met, the distribution
       of differences is always normally shaped

20. In order to calculate the estimated standard error of difference, all
   that need be known is (are)

   a. the means of the two samples
   b. the sizes of the two samples
   c. the standard deviation of the two samples
   *d. the estimated standard errors of the mean for each of the two
       samples

21. The t test may be used to evaluate the difference between

    *a. two sample means
     b. two or more sample means
     c. the mean and the standard deviation
     d. the mean and the variance

22. The t ratio may be used to evaluate whether

     a. two samples represent a single population
     b. two samples represent different populations
    *c. both of these
     d. neither of these

23. For the t test, the null hypothesis states that the samples

    *a. represent a single population
     b. represent different populations
     c. are of infinite size
     d. each have mean scores of zero

24. For the t test, degrees of freedom are based on

     a. the population sizes
    *b. the sample size
     c. the number of samples being compared
     d. none of these

25. When the degrees of freedom reach infinity, the t distribution

     a. becomes identical with the distribution of raw scores
     b. gets larger
    *c. approximates normality
     d. cannot be obtained

26. For the t test, the null hypothesis is always

     a. a function of sample size
     b. a function of variability
     c. a function of centrality
    *d. the same as the "chance" hypothesis

27. For the t test, the hypothesis of "no difference" is called the

     a. alternative hypothesis
    *b. null hypothesis
     c. central limit hypothesis
     d. hypothesis of association

28. When a difference is said to be "significant", it means that the differ-
    ence probably

     a. does not exist in the population
    *b. does exist in the population
     c. is no longer related to the population
     d. none of these

29. When a difference is considered "significant", it indicates that the difference is probably

    a. meaningful and profound
    b. due to chance
 *c. not due to chance alone
    d. none of these

30. Like the T score, the t ratio is a measure of

    a. individual performance
    b. how a single sample performed
    c. central tendency
 *d. none of these, since the T score and the t ratio involve totally different concepts

31. The difference between the T score and the t ratio is that

    a. the T score always results in a higher value than does the t ratio
    b. the T score refers to several sample means, whereas the t ratio only refers to two sample means
 *c. the T score is used as a measure of individual performance, whereas the t ratio evaluates the possibility of a performance difference between two groups
    d. none of these, since T and t are the same

32. For the t ratio, when the null hypothesis is rejected, then

 *a. the difference is assumed to be significant
    b. the difference is assumed to equal zero
    c. the difference is assumed to be positive
    d. none of these

33. For the t test, the null hypothesis is always stated in terms of

    a. the sample means
 *b. the population means
    c. both of these
    d. neither of these

34. The t ratio specifies how far the <u>difference</u> between the sample means deviates from

    a. an assumed mean of 50, in units of standard deviations
    b. an assumed mean of 100, in units of estimated standard errors of difference
 *c. an assumed mean of zero, in units of estimated standard errors of difference
    d. the standard deviation of the population

35. The t test for independent samples may only be used when

 *a. the selection of subjects for the first group does not depend in any way on the selection of subjects for the second group
    b. the subjects used in the two samples are matched on some relevant variable
    c. the same subjects are used twice
    d. the degrees of freedom are independent of the sample sizes

36. When the alternative hypothesis is accepted, then

   a. the sample means are assumed to be equal
   *b. the population means are assumed to be equal
   c. chance is rejected
   d. a significant difference has been established

37. Whenever the null hypothesis is rejected, then

   a. the alternative hypothesis must also be rejected
   *b. the alternative hypothesis must be accepted
   c. the alternative hypothesis must be tested separately
   d. none of these, since the null hypothesis and the alternative
       hypothesis are independent of each other

38. The statement that the difference between the two population means is
    zero, represents

   a. the alpha error
   b. the sampling error
   c. the alternative hypothesis
   *d. the null hypothesis

39. The alternative hypothesis for the t test is also called

   a. the hypothesis of association
   *b. the hypothesis of difference
   c. the null hypothesis
   d. none of these

40. When the null hypothesis is rejected, then

   a. the "chance" explanation is completely ruled out
   *b. the "chance" explanation, though not ruled out, becomes improbable
   c. the "chance" explanation is fully accepted
   d. the "chance" explanation becomes irrelevant

41. The alpha error is identical to the

   *a. Type 1 error
   b. Type 2 error
   c. Type 3 error
   d. none of these

42. According to the text, the value beyond which the alpha error should
    never be set, is

   a. .01
   *b. .05
   c. .50
   d. 1.00

43. The t distribution assumes normality only when

   *a. there are infinite degrees of freedom
   b. there is no alpha error
   c. the null hypothesis has been rejected
   d. none of these, since the t distribution can never be normal

44. With infinite sample sizes, t ratios of ±1.96

    a. include only the middle-most 68% of all t values
    b. include only the middle-most 50% of all t values
    c. include only the middle-most 5% of all t values
    *d. exclude only the most extreme 5% of all t values

45. With one degree of freedom, a significant t ratio will occur

    a. 1% of the time
    b. 99% of the time
    c. 68% of the time
    *d. none of these

46. If an independent t ratio is to be calculated for a two-group design,
    20 subjects in each group, then the degrees of freedom equal

    a. 1
    b. .05
    c. 40
    *d. 38

47. The t distribution assumes normality only when

    *a. there are infinite degrees of freedom
    b. there is no alpha error
    c. the null hypothesis has been rejected
    d. none of these, since the t distribution can never be normal

48. With infinite sample sizes, t ratios of ±1.96

    a. include only the middle-most 68% of all t values
    b. include only the middle-most 50% of all t values
    c. include only the middle-most 5% of all t values
    *d. exclude only the most extreme 5% of all t values

49. With one degree of freedom, a significant t ratio will occur

    a. 1% of the time
    b. 99% of the time
    c. 68% of the time
    *d. none of these

50. Every degree of freedom value specifies

    *a. a different t distribution
    b. the same t distribution
    c. that the t distribution must be assumed to be normal
    d. the number of sample groups being compared

51. If the tabled value for t, for a certain number of degrees of freedom,
    were 3.17, and the calculated value of t were 3.17, then

    a. Ho is accepted
    *b. Ho is rejected
    c. alpha becomes equal to zero
    d. the t distribution must be normal

52. To do a one-tail t test, as opposed to a two-tail,

   *a. the direction of the difference must always be specified beforehand
    b. the direction of the difference need only be specified after null
       has been rejected
    c. the direction of the difference must only be specified when null
       is accepted
    d. the direction of the difference becomes irrelevant

53. The sign of the t ratio only becomes important to the statistical
    decision when

    a. null is accepted
    b. the degrees of freedom are infinite
    c. the alpha error is set at .05 or less
   *d. calculating a one-tail t test

54. The t distributions deviate from normality when

    a. the null hypothesis is being tested
    b. the alpha error is less than .05
   *c. sample sizes become smaller
    c. none of these, since the t distribution never deviates from normality

55. Whenever the alternative hypothesis is written as "mean 1 is greater
    than mean 2", then

   *a. a one-tail t test is allowed
    b. only a two-tail t test is allowed
    c. an independent t test is not allowed
    d. sample sizes must be greater than 20

56. The only time a difference between two sample means may be called
    "significant" is when

    a. they are at least 10 points apart
    b. they differ by at least .05 points
    c. the first mean is larger than the second mean
   *d. the null hypothesis has been rejected

B. <u>True or False</u>: For the following, indicate T (True) or F (False)

57. When the two sample means are equal, the t ratio will always   T
    lead to an accept of the null hypothesis.

58. The mean of the distribution of differences becomes zero only   F
    when all sample pairs represent different populations.

59. When the direction of the difference between two sample   T
    means is not specified, we must use the two-tail t.

60. The larger the sample sizes, the greater the number of   T
    degrees of freedom.

61. With an infinite number of degrees of freedom the t   T
    distribution assumes normality.

62. When the null hypothesis is rejected, then the alternative   T
    hypothesis must be accepted.

63. The estimated standard error of difference estimates the value of the population mean.   F

64. The estimated standard error of difference may never assume a negative value.   T

65. The estimated standard error of difference is an estimate of the variability occurring within the entire distribution of differences.   T

66. The t ratio may only be calculated when the data are in ordinal form.   F

67. When all the possible sample pairs have been selected from a single population, the mean of the distribution of differences is expected to approximate zero.   T

68. When the null hypothesis is accepted, one may assume that the two sample groups represent a common population.   T

69. The central limit theorem suggests that the entire distribution of differences between pairs of successively drawn sample means approximated normality.   T

70. The distribution of differences is a distribution of sample measures.   T

71. The true standard error of difference is equal to the standard deviation of the entire sampling distribution of differences when all the sample pairs in the population have been measured.   T

72. The greater the number of degrees of freedom for the t ratio, the less the likelihood of rejecting the null hypothesis. F

73. As was true for the z test, the t ratio assumes that all the parameter values are known.   F

74. For a given t value, the likelihood of rejecting null increases when a two-tail, rather than a one-tail, t value is applied.   F

75. For the t ratio, degrees of freedom are based on the number of samples rather than the size of the samples.   F

76. When all the possible pairs of random sample means have been selected from the population, the mean of the sampling distribution of differences is a parameter.   T

77. The t ratio assumes that the two samples being compared are similar with respect to variability.   T

78. The t ratio, since it is non-parametric test, makes no assumptions regarding the shape of the population distribution from which the samples have been selected.   F

79. The t ratio may only be calculated when the data are in at least interval form.   T

80. The estimated standard error of difference is an interval   F
    estimate of the true mean of the distribution of underlying
    individual scores.

C. For the following questions, calculate the values.

81. A researcher selects a pair of random samples. In Group 1 the scores
    are 12, 6, 9, 10, 8, 7. In Group 2, the scores are, 10, 4, 7, 8, 7, 6.
    Find the standard error of difference.

    Ans. 1.20

82. A researcher selects a pair of random samples. In Group 1 the scores are
    20, 14, 16, 18, 9, 16, 18, 16, 15, 14.   In Group 2 the scores are 23, 20,
    21, 24, 18, 22, 24, 22, 20, 20. Find the standard error of difference.

    Ans. 1.13

83. A researcher selects a pair of random samples. In Group 1 the scores
    are 9, 12, 7, 8, 6. In Group 2 the scores are 6, 5, 7, 6, 5. Find
    the t ratio.

    Ans. 2.36

84. A researcher selects a pair of random samples. In Group 1 the scores
    are 25, 25, 24, 24, 23, 23, 22, 21, 20. In Group 2 the scores are 22,
    20, 20, 18, 15, 15, 12, 12, 10.
    a. Find the t ratio
    b. As a two-tail t, should Ho be rejected or accepted?
        If rejected, state the probability of the alpha error.
    c. Do the two groups represent a single population?

    Ans. a. 4.61
          b. Reject Ho, Significant at $P < .01$
          c. In all probability, they do not.

85. A researcher selects a pair of random samples. In Group 1 the scores are
    21, 19, 17, 13, 11, 9, 7. In Group 2 the scores are 20, 18, 15, 11, 11,
    8, 4.
    a. Find the t ratio.
    b. As a two-tail t, should Ho be rejected or accepted?
        If rejected, state the probability of the alpha error.
    c. Do the two groups represent a single population?

    Ans. a. .49
          b. Accept Ho
          c. Yes

86. A researcher selects a pair of random samples. In Group 1 the scores are
    14, 10, 10, 9, 8, 6, 4. In Group 2 the scores are 12, 10, 6, 5, 4, 2, 2.
    a. Find the t ratio.
    b. As a two-tail t, should Ho be rejected or accepted?
        If rejected, state the probability of the alpha error.
    c. Do the two groups represent a common population?

    Ans. a. 1.51
          b. Accept Ho
          c. Yes.

87. A researcher selects a pair of random samples. In Group 1 the scores are 3, 7, 6, 5. In Group 2 the scores are 4, 6, 2, 2.
a. Find the t ratio.
b. As a two-tail t, should Ho be rejected or accepted? If rejected, state the probability of the alpha error.
c. Do the two groups represent a single population?

    Ans. a. 1.36
          b. Accept Ho. Not significant.
          c. Yes

88. A researcher selects a pair of random samples. In Group 1 the scores are 10, 4, 12, 5, 4, 6, 8, 7. In Group 2 the scores are 6, 4, 9, 3, 2, 5, 7, 4.
a. Find the t ratio.
b. As a two-tail t, should Ho be rejected or accepted? If rejected, state the probability of the alpha error.
c. Do the two groups represent a single population?

    Ans. a. 1.54
          b. Accept Ho. Not significant
          c. Yes

89. A researcher selects a pair of random samples and predicts the beforehand that Group 2 will score higher than Group 1. The scores in Group 1 are 11, 10, 8, 3, 7, 1. The scores in Group 2 are 12, 11, 8, 4, 9, 2.
a. Find the t ratio.
b. As a one-tail t, should Ho be rejected or accepted? If rejected, state the probability of alpha error.
c. Do the two groups represent a single population?

    Ans. a. -.44
          b. Accept Ho. Not significant
          c. Yes

90. A researcher selects a pair of random samples and predicts beforehand that Group 1 will score higher than Group 2. The scores in Group 1 are 6, 7, 10, 9, 8. The scores in Group 2 are 3, 4, 9, 7, 5.
a. Find the t ratio.
b. As a one-tail t, should Ho be rejected or accepted? If rejected, state the probability of alpha error.
c. Do the two groups represent a single population?

    Ans. a. 1.86
          b. Accept Ho. Not significant
          c. Yes

For questions 91 through 94, use the following:

A researcher predicts that students will spend more time studying for a quiz if they are told that a high mark on that quiz will excuse them from writing a term paper. Two groups of college students were randomly selected from a large lecture course in art history. The students in Group 1 were simply told that they would have their first art-history quiz two days later. In Group 2, they were told the same thing, except that the promise of "no term paper" for high quiz performance was added. Just before taking the quiz, all students in both groups reported (in hours) the time they had spent preparing. In Group 1, the times were

6, 4, 9, 3, 2, 5, 7, 4. In Group 2 the times were 12, 5, 13, 5, 5, 7, 9, 6.

91. Find the standard error of difference.

   Ans. 1.39

92. Find the t ratio.

   Ans. -1.98

93. As a two-tail t, should Ho be rejected or accepted? If rejected, state the probability of alpha error.

   Ans. Accept Ho. Not significant.

94. As a one-tail t (since the direction of the difference was predicted) should Ho be rejected or accepted? If rejected, state the probability of alpha error.

   Ans. Reject Ho. Significant at P $<$.05

A. Multiple Choice Items

1. A maximum correlation is expressed as

    a. 100%
    b. 99
    c. ± 10.00
    *d. ± 1.00

2. The more a correlation deviates from zero,

    a. the more it is certain to be positive in sign
    b. the more it is certain to be negative in sign
    c. the more it is certain that the measured variables are
        independent of each other
    *d. the better its predictive accuracy

3. When two sets of measures are independent of each other, then the

    a. correlation between them must be negative
    b. correlation between them must be positive
    *c. correlation between them must be zero
    d. no attempt to calculate the correlation should be made

4. Of the following correlation coefficients, which expresses the weakest
    association?

    a. .10
    *b. 0
    c. -.50
    d. -1.00

5. Of the following correlation coefficients, which expresses the
    strongest association?

    a. .10
    b. 0
    c. -.50
    *d. -1.00

6. When two variables, A and B, are strongly correlated, it means that

    a. A has caused B
    b. B has caused A
    c. some third variable has caused both A and B to occur together
    *d. none of these

7. The correlation coefficient, in and of itself,

    a. never proves causation
    b. never rules out causation
    c. allows for better-than-chance predictions
    *d. all of these

8. The most common error in interpreting correlational research studies is in

   a. assuming that the data have been incorrectly reported
   b. assuming that the appropriate statistical analyses have been used
   *c. assuming that a causal factor has been isolated
   d. all of these

9. Each data point on a scatter plot represents

   a. the frequency of occurrence
   *b. a pair of scores
   c. a score on one measurement
   d. none of these

10. A scatter plot on which the array of points goes from upper left to lower right, indicates

   a. a positive correlation
   *b. a negative correlation
   c. a zero correlation
   d. all of these, depending on the strength of the correlation

11. The major reason for using the correlational techniques is to

   a. make cause-and-effect statements
   *b. make better-than-chance predictions
   c. identify a specific percentile
   d. establish a significant difference

12. On a scatter plot, the ordinate is used to represent

   *a. the scores on the Y measure
   b. the scores on the X measure
   c. the frequency of occurrence
   d. the product moment

13. When the array of points on a scatter plot slopes from lower left to upper right, then

   *a. the correlation is positive
   b. the correlation is negative
   c. there is no correlation
   d. no predictions can be made

14. The originator of the product-moment correlation technique was

   a. Gauss
   b. Pascal
   *c. Pearson
   d. Bodine

15. When variable A correlates highly with B, then

   a. A has caused B
   b. B has caused A
   *c. variable B correlates highly with A
   d. none of these

16. The correlation between parental income and the amount of financial aid awarded by the college to students should most probably be

    a. positive
    *b. negative
    c. zero
    d. none of these, since income is a nominal measure

17. Among elementary school children, the correlation between age and height would most probably be

    *a. positive
    b. negative
    c. zero
    d. non-linear

18. A "significant" correlation is one which

    a. is especially meaningful
    b. does not deviate from zero
    c. indicates a valid difference
    *d. can be generalized to the population

19. In order to establish the significance of a correlation, one must know the value of the correlation coefficient and also

    *a. the number of paired scores
    b. whether it relates to other measures
    c. whether it specifies the direction of the association
    d. the sign of the correlation

20. Negative correlations

    a. may never be significant
    b. may never be used for prediction
    c. may never generalize to the population
    *d. none of these

21. When a relationship is inverse it means that the correlation must be

    a. non-significant
    b. non-linear
    c. significant
    *d. negative

22. For the Pearson r, when Ho is rejected, it means that

    a. the correlation is positive
    b. the correlation is negative
    *c. the correlation is significant
    d. none of these

23. The Pearson r may be used to test the hypothesis of

    a. difference
    *b. association
    c. central limit
    d. all of these

24. When a correlation is not significant, it means that

    a. Ho has been accepted
    b. the correlation can't be generalized to the population
    c. the correlation is negative
    *d. a and b, but not c

25. When a correlation is discovered between two variables, A and B, it is possible, though not certain that

    a. A has caused B
    b. B has caused A
    c. X has caused A plus B
    *d. all of these

26. When the knowledge of one event allows for the prediction of another event, then the two events are

    a. significantly different
    b. causally related
    *c. correlated
    d. due to chance

27. When high scores on the first variable associate with high scores on the second, and low scores on the first associate with low scores on the second, then the correlation is

    a. non-existent
    *b. positive
    c. negative
    d. zero

For questions 28 through 33 use the following.

A researcher selects a random sample of college students and measures them on both the number of hours spent watching TV and grade-point average.

The results were as follows:

Subject #	Hours of TV X	GPA Y
1	50	1.90
2	20	2.20
3	19	2.40
4	10	3.00
5	7	2.90
6	15	2.50
7	5	3.50
8	40	1.95
9	30	2.00
10	0	3.90

28. The correlation between the two variables is generally

    a. positive
    *b. negative
    c. zero
    d. both positive and negative

29. If these data were to be placed on a scatter plot, the general
    slope of the array of points would be

    a. straight across
    *b. upper left to lower right
    c. lower left to upper right
    d. U shaped

30. Each point on the scatter plot portraying these data would indicate

    a. performance on GPA only
    b. hours of TV viewing only
    *c. both performance on GPA and hours of TV viewing
    d. none of these

31. The only valid conclusion one can draw from these data, is that

    a. TV viewing lowers GPA
    b. TV viewing increases GPA
    c. TV viewing is independent of GPA
    *d. A knowledge of TV viewing time allows for the prediction of GPA

32. If these data were placed on a scatter plot, the abscissa would represent

    *a. TV viewing time
    b. GPA
    c. the correlation
    d. frequency of occurrence

33. If these data were placed on a scatter plot, the ordinate would represent

    a. TV viewing time
    *b. GPA
    c. the correlation
    d. frequency of occurrence

34. The more any correlation value deviates from zero

    a. the more likely it is to be significant
    b. the stronger the association between the two variables
    c. the greater its predictive efficiency
    *d. all of these

35. In general, the array of points on a scatter plot tends to form the
    shape of

    a. a circle
    b. a rectangle
    c. a square
    *d. an oval

36. The reason for the typical shape assumed by the array of points in a scatter plot, is due to

   *a. the central tendency expected on the two distributions
    b. the wide variability expected on the two distributions
    c. the significant difference between the means of the two distributions
    d. the significant difference between the variabilities of the two distributions

37. For the Pearson r, the null hypothesis states that

    a. there is a significant correlation in the population
    b. there is no correlation in the sample
   *c. there is no correlation in the population
    d. the sample no longer represents the population

38. For the Pearson r, the alternative hypothesis states that

   *a. there is a significant correlation in the population
    b. there is no correlation in the sample
    c. there is no correlation in the population
    d. the sample no longer represents the population

39. Regardless of the degrees of freedom, any Pearson r of .90 or higher must be

    a. significant
    b. non-significant
    c. more than significant
   *d. none of these, since without the degrees of freedom significance cannot be determined

40. In doing a Pearson r on 20 pairs of scores, degrees of freedom would equal

    a. 20
   *b. 18
    c. 40
    d. 38

41. In doing a Pearson r with 10 degrees of freedom, there must have been

    a. 10 separate scores
    b. 22 separate scores
    c. 10 pairs of scores
   *d. 12 pairs of scores

42. For a given number of degrees of freedom, when the obtained r is equal to the critical tabled value of r, then

    a. Ho is accepted
   *b. Ho is rejected
    c. Ho is re-written as Ha
    d. Ho cannot be evaluated

43. When Ho is rejected for the Pearson r, then

    a. the correlation is not significant
   *b. the correlation is significant

c. the alpha error is eliminated
d. none of these, since when Ho is rejected no statement of
   significance is possible

44. With 5 degrees of freedom, the critical tabled value of the Pearson r
    is .75 for an .05 alpha error. If one were to obtain a Pearson r
    value of -.76, then

    a. Ho would be accepted
    *b. Ho would be rejected
    c. the alpha error would become negative
    d. none of these, since a negative Pearson r cannot be evaluated
       for significance

45. Any Pearson r which is significant at an alpha of .01, must also

    a. be significant at .001
    *b. be significant at .05
    c. be significant at any alpha level
    d. be positive

46. The Pearson r may only be used when the data form is <u>at least</u>

    a. nominal
    b. ordinal
    *c. interval
    d. ratio

47. For the Pearson r, as the sample size increases, so too

    *a. do the degrees of freedom
    b. does the alpha error
    c. do the number of measures taken on each subject
    c. none of these, since sample size is not relevant to the Pearson r

48. The proportion of the variability in the Y distribution which is
    accounted for by the variability in the X distribution, is determined by

    a. the Spearman r_s
    b. the null hypothesis
    c. the coefficient of contingency
    *d. the coefficient of determination

49. A Pearson r of .70 yields a coefficient-of-determination accuracy
    estimate of

    a. 70%
    b. 35%
    *c. 49%
    d. .05%

50. A Pearson r value of -.20

    a. can never be significant
    b. must always be significant
    c. cannot be evaluated
    *d. none of these

51. The Pearson r assumes that

    a. the samples are randomly selected
    b. the association between the variables is linear
    c. the measures do not depart from normality
 *d. all of these

52. Homoscedasticity refers to the

    a. central tendency within one of the two distributions
 *b. variability within the two distributions
    c. number of degrees of freedom
    d. all of these

53. When the underlying distribution of interval scores is violently skewed, the appropriate correlational technique should be

    a. the Pearson r
    b. the t test
 *c. the Spearman r_s
    d. none of these, since correlations cannot be computed for skewed distributions

54. When both sets of measures are in ordinal form, the appropriate correlational technique should be

    a. the Pearson r
    b. the t test
 *c. the Spearman r_s
    d. the coefficient of determination

55. When one set of measures is in interval form, and the other in ordinal, then the appropriate correlational technique should be

    a. the Pearson r
    b. the t test
 *c. the Spearman r_s
    d. the coefficient of determination

56. To calculate the degrees of freedom for the Spearman r_s, one must

    a. subtract 2 from the number scores
    b. subtract 2 from the number of paired scores
    c. add the number of scores to the constant 2
 *d. none of these

57. For the Spearman r_s, the null hypothesis states that

    a. there is no correlation in the sample
 *b. there is no correlation in the population
    c. the correlation is significant
    d. the alpha error is zero

58. For the Spearman r_s, in order to establish a significant correlation in the population

    a. Ho must be accepted
 *b. Ho must be rejected

c. Ho must be equal to the alpha error
d. none of these, since the Spearman r$_s$ cannot be used to infer population characteristics

59. For the Pearson r, rejecting Ho with an alpha of .05, means that

a. the correlation is not significant
b. there is no possibility that Ho should have been accepted
c. the probability is .95 that Ho should have been accepted
*d. the probability is .05 that Ho should have been accepted

60. The value of the Pearson r indicates

*a. the strength of the linear relationship between two sets of interval measures
b. the strength of the non-linear relationship between two sets of interval measures
c. the strength of the linear relationship between two sets of nominal measures
d. all of these

61. In order to rank-order the following IO scores, 120, 110, 110, 105, the appropriate rank would be

a. 1, 2, 3, 4
b. 1, 2, 4, 5
c. 1, 1.5, 1.5, 2, 3
*d. 1, 2.5, 2.5, 4

62. Whenever interval data are converted into ordinal data,

*a. the tied interval scores must be averaged, and assigned the same rank value
b. the tied interval scores must be eliminated from the analysis
c. the tied interval scores must be assigned different rank values
d. none of these, since interval data should not be converted into ordinal

63. Whenever ordinal data are converted into interval data,

a. the tied ordinal scores must be averaged, and assigned the same interval value
b. the tied ordinal scores must be eliminated from the analysis
c. the tied ordinal scores must be assigned different interval values
*d. none of these, since ordinal data should not be converted into interval

64. Whenever a correlation coefficient deviates significantly from zero, then

a. it may or may not be used for predictions, depending on its size
b. it may be used to establish totally accurate predictions
c. it may not be used for predictions
*d. it may be used for establishing better-than-chance predictions, regardless of its size

65. A significant correlation of -.40

   a. cannot be used for prediction
   b. predicts with an accuracy of 40%
   *c. predicts more accurately than a significant correlation of +.35
   d. predicts with less accuracy than a positive correlation of any size

66. The Spearman r_s may be appropriately used whenever

   a. both sets of measures are in ordinal form
   b. one set of measures is in interval form, and the other in ordinal form
   c. both sets of measures are in interval form, but the distributions are badly skewed
   *d. all of these

67. For the Pearson r, a non-significant correlation

   a. should not be used for prediction
   b. cannot be generalized to the population
   c. is simply due to chance
   *d. all of these

68. In order to make better-than-chance predictions, the Pearson r must be

   a. positive
   b. greater than .70
   c. greater than .90
   *d. significant

69. A significant Pearson r

   a. may be generalized to any population
   *b. may only be generalized to the population from which the sample measures were selected
   c. may only be generalized to finite populations
   d. may never be generalized to a population

B. True or False: For the following, indicate T (True) or F (False)

70. Whenever measures are in interval form, regardless of the   F
    shape of the distribution, the Pearson r may be used.

71. When portraying a correlation on a scatter plot, the array   T
    of data points usually forms an elliptical shape.

72. If the correlation between X and Y is zero, and the   T
    correlation between X and Z is zero, then the correlation
    between Y and Z should be zero.

73. The Spearman r_s is to ordinal data as the Pearson r is to   T
    interval data.

74. Significant correlations always predict with an accuracy   T
    which is better-than-chance.

75. The higher the value of the Pearson r, the lower the value   F
    of the coefficient of determination.

76. Whenever a correlation is significant, then a cause-and-effect   F
    relationship must be present.

77. On a scatter plot, the ordinate always displays the measures   T
    from the Y distribution.

78. A Pearson r value of .50 or higher must be significant,   F
    regardless of the sample size.

79. For the Pearson r, the sample size, not the value of r,   T
    determines the number of degrees of freedom.

80. For the Spearman r_s, the degrees of freedom are established   F
    in the same way as for the Pearson r.

81. A Pearson r of .80 means that the percentage of   F
    information about Y being contained in X is roughly 80.

82. A significant Pearson r (of any value) means that some   T
    information about Y is being contained in X.

83. All positive correlations predict with a higher level   F
    of accuracy than do all negative correlations.

84. For any correlation to be considered significant, the   T
    null hypothesis must first be rejected.

85. The Pearson r has the potential for yielding its   T
    highest numerical value when both sampling distributions,
    X and Y, represent the entire range of normally distributed
    values.

86. When attempting to assess the correlation between two   F
    distributions, X and Y, if either of the two variables
    fail to contain the high or low end of its distribution,
    the resulting coefficient will tend to over-estimate the
    true correlation in the population.

87. The restricted range phenomenon suggests that the value   T
    of the correlation between two variables will diminish as
    the distributions of scores being compared become more
    homogeneous.

88. For a given sample size, the Pearson r is more likely to   T
    show significance than is the Spearman r_s

89. The Pearson r is a non-parametric test of correlation.   F

90. The Spearman r_s is a parametric test of correlation.   F

C. For the following questions, calculate the values.

91. For the following, calculate the Pearson r.

X	Y
10	12
8	10
6	8
4	6
2	4

Ans. 1.00

92. For the following, calculate the Pearson r.

X	Y
10	2
8	4
6	6
4	8
2	10

Ans. -1.00

93. For the following scores,

   a. Calculate the Pearson r
   b. Should Ho be rejected or accepted? If rejected, state the probability of the alpha error.

X	Y
12	10
2	3
5	7
9	5
11	9
10	8
4	6
1	3

Ans. a. .87
      b. Reject Ho. Significant at $P < .01$

94. For the following scores,

   a. Calculate the Pearson r
   b. Should Ho be rejected or accepted? If rejected, state the probability of the alpha error.

X	Y
10	8
9	8
7	6
4	3
8	7
2	1
1	2
10	11

Ans. a. .96
      b. Reject Ho. Significant at $P < .01$

95. For the following scores,

    a. Calculate the Pearson r
    b. Should Ho be rejected or accepted? If rejected, state the probability of the alpha error.

X	Y
10	5
10	7
8	10
6	2
4	1
2	9
1	10

    Ans. a. -.17
          b. Accept Ho. Not significant

96. For the following scores,

    a. Calculate the Pearson r
    b. Should Ho be rejected or accepted? If rejected, state the probability of the alpha error.

X	Y
12	6
6	7
9	8
10	7
8	4
7	10
8	10
10	10

    Ans. a. -.15
          b. Accept Ho. Not significant

97. For the following scores,

    a. Calculate the Pearson r
    b. Should Ho be rejected or accepted? If rejected, state the probability of the alpha error.

X	Y
20	1
15	4
15	9
12	9
10	13
10	14
5	14
3	21

    Ans. a. -.94
          b. Reject Ho. Significant at $P < .01$

98. For the following scores,

   a. Calculate the Pearson r
   b. Should Ho be rejected or accepted? If rejected, state the probability of alpha error.

X	Y
4	5
10	10
6	5
12	10
10	10
2	4
8	7

   Ans. a. .95
        b. Reject Ho. Significant at $P < .01$

99. For the following ranks,

   a. Calculate the Spearman r_s

   b. Should Ho be rejected or accepted? If rejected, state the probability of alpha error.

R_1	R_2
2.5	1
2.5	2
1.0	5
5.5	7
7.0	8
8.0	6
4.0	4
5.5	3

   Ans. a. .62
        b. Accept Ho. Not significant

100. For the following ranks,

   a. Calculate the Spearman r_s

   b. Should Ho be rejected or accepted? If rejected, state the probability of alpha error.

R_1	R_2
4.0	5
8.5	4
6.0	3
1.0	1
2.5	2
2.5	6
6.0	8
8.5	7
6.0	9
10.0	10

   Ans. a. .65
        b. Reject Ho. Significant at $P < .05$

101. A researcher wishes to test the hypothesis that there is a correlation between IQ and math ability. A random sample of 8 subjects was selected. Each subject was given an IQ test, and then rank-ordered in terms of mathematical ability.

IQ Score	Math Rank
130	1
92	5
115	4
115	3
82	6
82	7
60	8
120	2

    a. Calculate the appropriate correlation.
    b. Should Ho be rejected or accepted? If rejected, state the probability of alpha error.

    Ans. a. r_s = .98

           b. Reject Ho. Significant at $P < .01$

102. A researcher is interested in testing the hypothesis that income is negatively related to family size. A random sample of 10 families was selected from the population of a large mid-western city. All families were assessed on both their per-family income and their numbers of children.

The data follow:

Family	Per-family income	Number of children
A	$190,000	2
B	$30,000	6
C	$19,000	7
D	$40,000	3
E	$23,000	6
F	$40,000	4
G	$25,000	5
H	$40,000	3
I	$28,000	1
J	$30,000	5

Since the income distribution was badly skewed, it was decided not to use the Pearson r.

    a. Calculate the correlation
    b. Should Ho be rejected or accepted? If Ho is rejected, state the probability of alpha error.

    Ans. a. r_s = -.62

           b. Accept Ho. Not significant

For questions 103 through 107 use the following:

A researcher wishes to find out whether there is a dependable relationship between the severity of earthquakes and temperature for the 7 days immediately preceding the quake. A sample of 10 measured earthquakes was randomly selected from those recorded since 1965. For each area both the Richter value (higher values meaning more severe quakes) and the mean temperature for the 7 days preceding the quakes were recorded. The data follow:

Area	Richter Scale Value	Mean Temperature
A	8.0	65
B	7.0	67
C	4.9	70
D	6.5	66
E	5.0	65
F	5.5	60
G	5.0	63
H	4.5	64
I	5.0	65
J	2.0	65

Neither distribution appears skewed.

103. Calculate the correlation.

Ans. r = .08

104. How many degrees of freedom should be assigned?

Ans. 8

105. Should Ho be rejected or accepted?

Ans. Accepted

106. If rejected, state the probability of the alpha error.

Ans. Ho was accepted

107. Can the severity of earthquakes be predicted on the basis of temperature?

Ans. No

A. Multiple Choice Items

1. The statement that "one can prove anything with statistice" is only true when

    a. correlational research has been used
    b. post-facto research has been used
    c. the data have been cross-referenced
    *d. the reader is totally naive regarding statistical procedures

2. The most common error in reading and interpreting research studies is in

    a. assuming that the data have been incorrectly reported
    b. assuming that the correct statistical tests have been used
    *c. assuming that a causal factor has been isolated
    d. all of these

3. In any antecedent-consequent relationship, the independent variable

    *a. precedes the dependent variable
    b. follows the dependent variable
    c. occurs simultaneously with the dependent variable
    d. none of these

4. In any antecedent-consequent relationship, the dependent variable

    a. precedes the independent variable
    *b. follows the independent variable
    c. occurs simultaneously with the independent variable
    d. none of these

5. In correlational research, the independent variable is placed

    *a. on the abscissa
    b. on the ordinate
    c. on each data point
    d. none of these, since correlational research can never be graphed

6. In correlational research, whichever variable one predicts from is called

    a. the criterion variable
    *b. the independent variable
    c. the dependent variable
    d. the control variable

7. When it is assumed that information about the X variable may be used to predict the Y variable, then the X variable is

    *a. the independent variable
    b. the dependent variable
    c. the control variable
    d. the criterion variable

8. In any input-output relationship, the dependent variable is considered
   to be

   a. the input
   *b. the output
   c. the relationship itself between the two measured variables
   d. all of these, depending on the type of research

9. An example of an assigned independent variable would be

   a. IQ
   b. race
   c. sex
   *d. all of these

10. An example of a manipulated independent variable would be

    a. IQ
    b. income level
    c. amount of education
    *d. none of these

11. When the researcher has actively altered the environmental conditions,
    then the independent variable has been

    a. assigned
    *b. manipulated
    c. confounded
    d. strengthened

12. In a study on the effects of TV violence on viewer aggressiveness, the
    dependent variable would be the

    a. control group
    b. TV violence
    *c. viewer aggressiveness
    d. experimental group

13. In a study on whether increasing illumination increases worker
    productivity, the independent variable would be the

    *a. illumination levels
    b. worker productivity rates
    c. causal relationship
    d. experimental group

14. If a researcher wished to assess whether or not a certain drug will
    increase IQ scores, the independent variable would be the

    *a. drug levels
    b. IQ scores
    c. IQ test
    d. subjects whose IQ's were changed

15. One should not infer a direct cause-and-effect relationship when the
    research method is

    a. experimental   c. double-blind
    *b. post-facto   d. after-only

16. The two basic types of research are

    a. post-facto and correlational
    b. post-facto and cross-sectional
    *c. post-facto and experimental
    d. post-facto and longitudinal

17. When subjects are measured, then followed through the years and measured again, the research technique is called

    *a. longitudinal
    b. cross-sectional
    c. matched group
    d. controlled manipulation

18. When doing human-research studies on the long-term effects of growth and development, it is best to use

    *a. longitudinal research
    b. cross-sectional research
    c. after-only research
    d. anecdotal research

19. In experimental research, the independent variable is

    a. the response made by the subject
    b. the group receiving the placebo
    *c. actively manipulated by the experimenter
    d. the control group

20. In experimental research on humans, the independent variable is

    a. some form of stimulus presented to the subjects
    b. under the full, active control of the experimenter
    c. the potential causal half of the cause-and-effect relationship
    *d. all of these

21. When neither the subjects nor the experimenter are aware of which group is experimental and which is control, then the study is said to be

    a. contaminated
    b. confounded
    c. concealed
    *d. double-blind

22. In experimental research on humans, the dependent variable is

    a. manipulated by the experimenter
    b. the causal half of the cause-and-effect relationship
    c. some form of stimulus
    *d. a measure of the subject's response

23. In a study on whether college graduates earn more money then non-college graduates, the research method is almost certainly

    *a. post-facto
    b. experimental
    c. after-only
    d. before-after

24. The best way to distinguish between experimental and post-facto research is to discover whether

    a. the independent variable has been confounded
    *b. the independent variable has been manipulated or assigned
    c. the dependent variable has been manipulated or assigned
    d. the appropriate statistical test has been used

25. In the study, cited in the text, of the relationship between the amount of time a teacher spends smiling and the achievement level of the students, it was shown that

    a. the less time a teacher smiles, the better the students do on an achievement test
    *b. the more time a teacher smiles, the better the students do on an achievement test
    c. the time a teacher spends smiling is independent of student achievement
    d. a smiling teacher causes a student to get better grades

In the following questions (26 through 30), you are to identify the alternative which is not appropriately grouped with the others

26. a. after-only
    b. before-after
    *c. post-facto
    d. matched-subjects

27. a. independent variable
    b. assigned variable
    c. manipulated variable
    *d. dependent variable

28. a. response measure
    *b. independent variable
    c. dependent variable
    d. out-put measure

29. a. correlation
    b. association
    c. prediction
    *d. experimental method

30. *a. correlation
    b. cause-and-effect relationship
    c. experimental method
    d. manipulated independent variable

31. When a researcher randomly selects equivalent groups, and then exposes them to different stimulus conditions, and then measures them to see if significant differences can be observed, the total procedure is an example of

    *a. experimental research
    b. post-facto research
    c. cross-sectional research
    d. none of these

32. The basic goal of good post-facto research is <u>always</u>

   a. to establish a causal factor
   b. to test the hypothesis of difference
   c. to test the hypothesis of association
   *d. to make better-than-chance predictions

33. When a post-facto relationship is found between two variables A and B, it is always possible, though <u>not certain</u>, that

   a. A caused B
   b. B caused A
   c. a third variable, X, has caused A plus B
   *d. all of these

34. A study which compares the growth in the number of PTA mothers to the number of small business failures would be an example of

   a. experimental research
   *b. post-facto research
   c. after-only research
   d. before-after research

35. When using the post-facto method, one may test the hypothesis of

   a. difference
   b. association
   *c. both of these
   d. neither of these

36. When using the experimental method, the final goal is to test the hypothesis of

   *a. difference
   b. association
   c. both of these
   d. neither of these

Questions 37 through 42 will be bases on the following study:

A researcher wishes to test whether the drug, magnesium pemoline, has any influence on intelligence. Two groups of subjects are randomly selected from the population of Omega University students. Group A is given the magnesium pemoline and then tested on the Stanford-Binet IQ test. Group B is given a placebo and, then, also tested on the Stanford-Binet. Both groups are tested under identical environmental conditions.

37. The study described above is an example of

   *a. experimental research
   b. post-facto research
   c. correlational research
   d. longitudinal research

38. The design of this study is an example of

   *a. after-only method   c. the matched-subjects method
   b. the before-after method   d. the repeated measure method

39. The independent variable in this study is (are) the

    a. Stanford-Binet test
*b. magnesium pemoline
    c. control group
    d. IQ scores

40. The group which received the placebo is called

    a. the experimental group
*b. the control group
    c. the matched group
    d. the model group

41. The dependent variable in this study is (are) the

    a. magnesium pemoline
    b. testing conditions
*c. IQ scores
    d. there was no dependent variable in this study

42. If the IQ scores in Group A had been significantly higher than those in Group B, we may conclude that

*a. the magnesium pemoline probably caused an increase in IQ scores
    b. the magnesium pemoline probably caused a decrease in IQ scores
    c. cause and effect statements cannot be inferred from this study
    d. none of these

43. When subjects are measured on some trait they already possess, and are then categorized on the basis of that trait, the independent variable has been

*a. assigned
    b. manipulated
    c. confounded
    d. actively altered by the experimenter

44. When it is established that a change in the independent variable actually produces a change in the dependent variable , then the research must be

    a. post-facto
    b. cross-sectional
*c. experimental
    d. none of these

45. In experimental research, when the group is used as both an experimental and control group, the research design is

    a. matched-subjects
*b. before-after
    c. after-only
    d. none of these

46. With the matched-subjects design, the subjects are equated on some variable which is assumed to have an influence on the

    a. independent variable   c. both of these
*b. dependent variable   d. neither of these

47. The whole point of using one of the various experimental designs is to

    *a. create equivalent groups of subjects
    b. randomize the alpha error
    c. prevent any sampling error
    d. prevent any possibility of alpha error

48. When a t test is applied to experimental research data, the groups are being compared with regard to their performances on the

    a. independent variable
    *b. dependent variable
    c. confounding variable
    d. controlled variable

Questions 49 through 54 will be based on the following:

A researcher wishes to test the hypothesis that intelligence is a sex-linked characteristic. A random sample of 1000 women is selected and given IQ tests. Similarly, a random sample of 1000 men is selected and also given IQ tests. The mean IQ's of the two groups are compared and the difference is found to be significantly in favor of the females.

49. This study proves that

    *a. a non-chance difference exists between male and female IQ's
    b. being female causes one to have a higher IQ
    c. being male causes one to have a lower IQ
    d. none of these

50. The research technique used in this study is an example of

    a. experimental research
    *b. post-facto research
    c. longitudinal research
    d. b and c, but not a

51. In this study, the variable being manipulated by the researcher is

    a. sex
    b. intelligence
    c. the IQ tests
    *d. none of these

52. This study proves that

    a. a causal relationship exists between sex and intelligence
    b. a causal relationship exists between intelligence and sex
    c. sex and intelligence interact to cause an effect above and beyond either of the variables taken separately
    *d. this study does not address the question of causality, since it is post-facto research

53. The results of this study suggest that

    *a. sex may be used to predict IQ
    b. IQ is independent of sex
    c. sex is one of the causal factors in producing one's IQ
    d. the IQ difference should not be generalized to the population from which the sample was selected

54. The appropriate statistical test for the analysis of these data would be the

  a. Pearson r
  b. Spearman r_s
  *c. t test
  d. none of these, since IQ scores form only nominal data

55. When the experimenatl method has been used, and a significant difference is established between the means of two sample groups, then it is highly probable that

  a. the sample groups could not have been equivalent to start with
  *b. the sample groups now represent different populations
  c. the sample groups still represent a single population
  d. a Pearson r analysis has been performed

56. When a sample group is being evaluated on the basis of two disparate measures, such as income and IQ, then which of the following statistical tests could not be used.

  a. the Pearson r
  b. the Spearman r_s
  *c. the t test
  d. the coefficient of determination

57. When the achievement levels of two groups of college seniors are being evaluated on the basis of whether or not the students had previously attended a public secondary school, then the research is

  a. experimental
  b. before-after
  c. after-only
  *d. post-facto

58. The covariance technique attempts to

  a. establish a significant difference between measures of the independent and dependent variables
  b. establish a significant difference between two disparate measures, such as height and weight
  *c. create equivalent groups of subjects, after the fact
  d. manipulate both the independent and dependent variables

59. When using the covariance technique, the researcher hopes to

  *a. create statistical controls on one or more of the variables
  b. create statistical controls on one or more of the variables which might influence the independent variable
  c. create statistical controls on one or more of the variables which might influence the various control variables
  d. prevent any possibility of sampling bias

60. When subjects change their behavior simply as a result of the experimenter paying attention to them, this is called

  a. the halo effect   c. the Rosenthal effect
  *b. the Hawthorne effect   d. the Zeigarnik effect

61. When a person is viewed as being positive in one area, and then is assumed to be positive in other areas, this is called

    a. the double-blind error
    b. the nominal fallacy
    c. the beta error
  *d. the halo effect

62. The before-after experimental design may lead to ambiguous results unless

    a. the subjects are matched on some relevent variable
    b. the dependent variable is measured only after the introduction of the independent variable
    c. the alpha error is increased to at least .50
  *d. there is a separate control group

63. The potential for the Hawthorne effect is most pronounced when the researcher is using

    a. the after-only design
    b. the matched-subjects design
  *c. the before-after design
    d. an assigned independent variable

64. The best way to prevent the Hawthorne effect is to use

    a. post-factor research technique
    b. objective observers
  *c. a separate control group
    d. none of these, since preventing the Hawthorne effect is itself a major research error

65. When the researcher is unable to examine the pure effects of the independent variable, then the independent variable is said to be

    a. manipulated
  *b. confounded
    c. held constant in the control group
    d. none of these

66. In experimental research, whenever extraneous influences cause changes on the dependent variable, then

    a. the independent variable has not been properly manipulated
    b. the dependent variable has been confounded
    c. the dependent variable has not been adequately measured
  *d. the independent variable has been confounded

67. The independent variable is said to have been confounded whenever

  *a. the response differences could have been caused by other factors
    b. the response differences are significant
    c. null is rejected
    d. null is accepted

68. In experimental research, cause-and-effect statements should not be made unless

    a. the sample groups are significantly different before the independent variable is introduced
  *b. the sample groups are significantly different after the independent variable is introduced
    c. the sample groups represent a common population after the independent variable is introduced
    d. the null hypothesis is accepted

Questions 69 through 75 will be based on the following:

A researcher was interested in discovering whether attitude changes can be more effectively brought about when persons are made to feel part of the decision making process. A group of women was selected and randomly assigned to one of two groups, one group being placed in a large lecture hall, and the other in a small discussion-group setting. In the lecture setting, a speaker exhorted the women to use less expensive cuts of meat, whereas in the small-group setting a different group leader, although raising the same issues as the lecture leader had, also encouraged the subjects to participate in the discussion and offer suggestions. Several weeks later both groups of women were checked at home to determine whether they were indeed using the meat cuts which had been urged. Only 3% of the lecture group members had the meat cuts, whereas 32% of the discussion group members had the meat cuts. The difference was clearly significant.

69. The research method involved was

    a. post-facto
    b. longitudinal
  *c. experimental
    d. designed to eliminate any possibility of alpha error

70. The design of the study was

  *a. after-only
    b. before-after
    c. matched-subjects
    d. none of these

71. Whether the subjects were subjected to the lecture method or the group discussion method, defined the

    a. control group
    b. assigned variable
    c. dependent variable
  *d. independent variable

72. The independent variable was

    a. assigned
  *b. manipulated
    c. held constant
    d. accounted for by the difference in group variability

73. Whether or not the women later had the meat cuts defined

   a. the assigned independent variable
   b. the manipulated independent variable
   c. the error scores
   *d. the dependent variable

74. The fact that the two groups were led by different persons created the possibility of incurring

   a. beta error
   b. the halo effect
   c. the Hawthorne effect
   *d. confounding variables

75. The fact that the two groups differed significantly regarding whether or not they had the meat cuts, means that

   a. Ho was accepted
   b. Ho was never tested
   *c. Ho was rejected
   d. the dependent variable was not affected

76. In evaluating the results of experimental research, secondary variance is considered to be

   a. an essential component of the design
   b. a result of the action of the independent variable
   *c. the result of the influence of any uncontrolled, or confounding, variables
   d. the error term in the F ratio

77. When secondary variance is allowed to occur in experimental research,

   a. the design is assumed to have internal validity
   b. the design is assumed to have external validity
   c. the design is assumed to be tightly controlled
   *d. the design is assumed to be "flawed"

78. When the design of an experiment simulates real-life conditions, it is said to be high in

   a. internal validity
   *b. external validity
   c. internal reliability
   d. all of these

79. When the design of an experiment is such that the influence of the independent variable can be unambiguously interpreted, the experiment is said to be high in

   *a. internal validity
   b. external validity
   c. external reliability
   d. all of these

80. According to the text, the major factor in achieving internal validity is in the correct use of

    a. statistical techniques of analysis
    b. representative sampling methods
    c. inductive logic
 *d. an adequate control group

81. A study which produces large amounts of secondary variance will probably be found to be extremely low in

    a. sampling error
    b. alpha error
    c. random error
 *d. internal validity

B. True or False: For the following, indicate T (True) or F (False)

82. Experimental methodology demands the use of a manipulated independent variable.   T

83. Whenever two separate sample groups are being compared, the research must be experimental.   F

84. Whenever the independent variable has been assigned, the research must be post-facto.   T

85. The only way to establish a unidirectional relationship between the independent variables is to use the Pearson r.   F

86. The main purpose of post-facto research is to establish equivalent groups subjects.   F

87. If a researcher establishes a significant correlation in order to predict college grades on the basis of SAT scores, the SAT scores would be the independent variable.   T

88. It is virtually impossible to manipulate such variables as age, sex, race or income.   T

89. Experimental research only allows for the testing of the hypothesis of association.   F

90. In experimental research, the dependent variable always defines the differences in the treatment conditions undergone by the subjects.   F

91. If subjects were measured on both height and weight, the researcher would most likely evaluate the results by using the t test.   F

92. When groups of subjects are equal to begin with, but are then treated differently by the experimenter, the research technique is post-facto.   F

93. One method which is used in order to create equivalent groups of subjects is the matched-subjects design.   T

94. The after-only, before-after or matched-subjects designs may be used when conducting experimental research.   T

95. Post-facto research techniques may only be used to test the hypothesis of difference.   F

96. Whenever the hypothesis of difference is tested, the research method must have been experimental.   F

97. In order to establish that one group of subjects is significantly taller than another group, the Pearson r must be used.   F

98. Correlational research may never be post-facto.   F

99. A study designed to test the effect of economic inflation on personal income, would define personal income as the independent variable.   F

100. In correlational research, the dependent variable is always the variable being predicted.   T

101. In the antecedent-consequent relationship, the dependent variable is always the antecedent variable.   F

102. The choice of which statistical test to use is always determined by whether the research is experimental or post-facto.   F

103. As long as the hypothesis of difference is being tested, the t test may be used to evaluate either post-facto or experimental data.   T

104. When an independent variable is actively manipulated, the research must be post-facto.   F

105. The Hawthorne effect occurs whenever a group of subjects changes as a direct result of the flattery and attention received from the experimenter.   T

106. The Hawthorne effect is most likely to occur when the research design is after-only.   F

107. An experiment which is high in internal validity is usually relatively free of the effects of confounding variables.   T

108. Primary variance is assumed to result from the action of the independent variable.   T

109. The technique of counterbalancing assures that external validity will be minimized.   F

110. The problem produced by sequencing effects is minimized when subjects are given several tasks to perform in a repeated-measure design.   F

111. A major issue in the design of an effective experiment is the elimination of primary variance.   F

CHAPTER 12
ANALYSIS OF VARIANCE

A. Multiple Choice Items

1. The F ratio was developed by

    a. William Sealy Gossett
   *b. Sir Ronald Fisher
    c. Karl Pearson
    d. James J. Ancova

2. The F ratio may be used to assess differences between (among)

    a. two sample means
    b. three sample means
    c. four sample means
   *d. all of these

3. Analysis of experimental data by the F ratio means that the independent variable could have been manipulated

    a. at only two levels
   *b. at two or more levels
    c. at only three levels
    d. none of these, since F cannot handle experimental data

4. Doing successive t tests within the context of a single experiment

    a. is theoretically the same as doing an F ratio
    b. is theoretically the same as doing a Pearson r
    c. is theoretically the same as doing a Spearman r_s
   *d. inflates the alpha error

5. With a two-group experimental design, the independent variable has been manipulated at

    a. one level
   *b. two levels
    c. three levels
    d. fifteen levels

6. Comparing all means from a four-group design would require the calculation of

    a. four t tests
   *b. six t tests
    c. one t test
    d. fifteen t tests

7. If one had to calculate 15 successive t tests, it would mean

    a. testing Ho 5 times
    b. testing Ho once
   *c. testing Ho 15 times
    d. none of these, since t never tests Ho

8. With the t test, as the number of decisions to reject Ho increases, so too

    a. does the number of degrees of freedom
    b. does the sampling error
    *c. does the alpha error
    d. all of these

9. With the F ratio, the overall hypothesis among 4 group means may be tested by making

    a. 4 statistical decisions
    b. 3 statistical decisions
    c. 2 statistical decisions
    *d. 1 statistical decision

10. For the F ratio, if alpha is set at .05, it remains at .05 if comparisons are made between (among)

    a. 2 group means
    b. 10 group means
    c. 45 group means
    *d. all of these

11. The alternative hypothesis for the F ratio is that the sample means

    a. represent a single population
    b. represent completely different populations
    *c. do not all represent a single population
    d. none of these

12. When the distribution of raw scores within a sample forms a leptokurtic shape, then

    *a. the variance within the sample is small
    b. the variance within the sample is large
    c. the variance within the sample is negative
    d. the variance within the sample equals the standard deviation

13. When the distribution of scores within a sample forms a platykurtic shape, then

    a. the variance within the sample is small
    *b. the variance within the sample is large
    c. the variance within the sample is negative
    d. the variance within the sample equals the standard deviation

14. The only time the variance becomes equal to the standard deviation is when

    a. the variance is small
    b. the variance is large
    c. the variance is eliminated
    *d. the variance is equal to 1.00

15. The SS, sum of squares, is equal to

    a. the sum of the squared scores
    b. the sum of the scores, squared
    *c. the sum of the squared deviations of all the scores from the mean
    d. the sum of the squared deviations of all the scores from the mean, divided by the degrees of freedom

16. When the SS, sum of squares, is large, so too is the

    a. standard deviation
    b. variance
    *c. both of these
    d. neither of these

17. The smallest possible value for the SS, sum of squares, is

    a. -5.00
    *b. 0
    c. .01
    d. 1.00

18. The concept of "total variability" is based on

    *a. how far the scores in all groups deviate from the total mean
    b. how far the sample means deviatte from each other
    c. how far the scores in a single group deviate from their own group mean
    d. how far each sample mean deviates from the total mean

19. The concept of "between variability" is based on

    a. how far the scores in all groups deviate from the total mean
    b. how far the scores in a single group deviate from their own group mean
    *c. how far each sample mean deviates from the total mean
    d. all of these, depending on the between degrees of freedom

20. The concept of "within variability" is based on

    a. how far the scores in all groups deviate from the total mean
    *b. how far the scores deviate from their own sample means
    c. how far each sample mean deviates from the total mean
    d. none of these

21. When the variance within a sample group is equal to 16, then the
    standard deviation for that sample is equal to

    a. 16
    b. 8
    c. 1.00
    *d. none of these

22. The sums of squares components relate such that SS_t is equal to

    a. SS_B c. $SS_W - SS_B$

    *b. $SS_B + SS_W$ d. none of these

23. The sums of squares components relate such that SS_B is equal to

    a. SS_W c. $SS_t + SS_B$

    *b. $SS_t - SS_W$ d. none of these

24. The sum of squares components relate such that SS_W is equal to

   a. SS_t

   b. $SS_t + SS_B$

   *c. $SS_t - SS_B$

   d. $SS_t - SS_c$

25. When the between sum of squares is relatively large, then the shape of the sampling distribution is necessarily

   a. leptokurtic
   b. platykurtic
   c. mesokurtic
   *d. none of these

26. When the within sum of squares is relatively large, then the shape of the sampling distribution is necessarily

   a. leptokurtic
   *b. platykurtic
   c. mesokurtic
   d. none of these

27. The greater the value of the F ratio,

   a. the more the sample distributions overlap
   *b. the less the sample distributions overlap
   c. the larger the sum of squares within groups
   d. none of these

28. The greater the sum of squares within groups

   a. the more the sample means deviate from the total mean
   b. the more the sample means deviate from each other
   c. the more the individual scores deviate from the total mean
   *d. none of these

29. The less overlap there is among the various sample-group distributions

   *a. the larger the F ratio
   b. the smaller the F ratio
   c. the greater the degrees of freedom
   d. none of these

30. An F ratio of 5, tells us specifically that the variance between groups is

   a. 5 times smaller than the variance within
   *b. 5 times larger than the variance within
   c. 5 times smaller than the total variance
   d. 5 times larger than the total variance

31. If the F ratio were performed on a two-group design and F was equal to 9, then t would be equal to

   a. 81
   b. 9
   *c. 3
   d. none of these

32. If the F ratio were performed on a four-group design and F was equal to 4, then t would be equal to

    a. 16
    b. 4
    c. 2
  *d. none of these

33. The mean square (MS) is <u>always</u> equal to (when based on SS/df)

    a. the square of the total mean
    b. the sum of the squares of the separate group means
    c. the variance squared
  *d. the variance

34. The larger the F ratio

    a. the more likely the samples represent a common population
  *b. the less likely the samples represent a common population
    c. the more likely that the between sum of squares is small
    d. the more likely that the within sum of squares is large

35. The greater the value of the MS between groups,

  *a. the more likely Ho will be rejected
    b. the less likely Ho will be rejected
    c. the more likely the various group means will equal each other
    d. none of these

36. If a significant F ratio is obtained, then

    a. Ho must be accepted
  *b. Ho must be rejected
    c. Ha must be rejected
    d. there must be at least four sample means

37. When four leptokurtic sampling distributions show no overlap whatever, then

    a. the MS within is likely to be large
    b. the MS between is likely to be small
  *c. the F ratio is likely to be significant
    d. there must be zero degrees of freedom

38. When doing an F ratio on a four-group design, 4 subjects in each group, the between degrees of freedom will equal

    a. the MS between
    b. 4
  *c. 3
    d. 12

39. When doing an F ratio on a three-group design, 5 subjects in each group, the within degrees of freedom will equal

    a. the MS within
    b. 2
    c. 5
  *d. none of these

40. When doing an F ratio, subtracting the number of groups from the total number of subjects yields the

    a. alpha error
    b. between degrees of freedom
    *c. within degrees of freedom
    d. total degrees of freedom

41. When doing an F ratio, subtracting the constant, 1, from the total number of sample groups yields the

    a. alpha error
    *b. between degrees of freedom
    c. within degrees of freedom
    d. total degrees of freedom

42. Dividing the sum of squares(SS) by the degrees of freedom, yields the

    a. F ratio
    b. alpha error
    *c. the mean square
    d. ANOVA

43. Dividing the MS between by the MS within, yields the

    *a. F ratio
    b. alpha error
    c. variance
    d. ANOVA

44. When the calculated F ratio is equal to or greater than the critical, tabled value of F for a given number of degrees of freedom, then

    a. alpha is inflated
    b. Ho is accepted
    *c. Ho is rejected
    d. none of these

45. The F ratio can never be significant unless

    a. the MS between is significantly smaller than the MS within
    b. the MS between is equal to the MS within
    *c. the MS between is significantly larger than the MS within
    d. none of these

46. When analyzing experimental research via the F ratio, the action of the independent variable is most clearly shown in the value of the

    a. MS total
    b. MS within
    *c. MS between
    d. degrees of freedom

47. When analyzing experimental research via the F raio, random error and individual differences among the subjects is most clearly shown in the value of the

    a. MS total   c. MS between
    *b. MS within   d. degrees of freedom

48. When analyzing experimental research via the F ratio, the number of sample groups, and the number of subjects in each sample group, are most clearly shown in the value of the

   a. MS total
   b. MS within
   c. MS between
  *d. degrees of freedom

49. If the MS between equals 10, and the MS within equals 5, then the F ratio equals

   a. 15.00
   b. .50
  *c. 2.00
   d. cannot tell from the above information

50. If the MS between equals 10, and the MS within equals 10, the total degrees of freedom are equal to

   a. 1
   b. 20
   c. 0
  *d. cannot tell from the above information

51. The one-way ANOVA may only be used when

   a. the direction of the difference is specified
   b. the F ratio is significant
   c. there are more than 3 sample groups
  *d. there is only one independent variable

52. Tukey's HSD is used in order to

   a. establish the significance of the overall F ratio
   b. allocate the degrees of freedom
   c. establish the alpha error
  *d. none of these

53. Once an F ratio has been found not to be significant, we must immediately

   a. apply Tukey's HSD
   b. increase the alpha error
   c. re-allocate the degrees of freedom
  *d. none of these

54. Once an F ratio is found to be significant, then

   a. each sample mean must represent a differenct population
   b. each sample mean must represent a single population
   c. each sample mean deviates by the same amount
  *d. none of these

55. When analyzing a significant ANOVA, in order to establish precisely where the sample differences may have occurred, we may

    *a. apply the HSD
    b. reduce the alpha error
    c. calculate the coefficient of determination
    d. none of these, since a significant F indicates precisely where the sample differences can be found

56. If the tabled value for F, for a given number of degrees of freedom, were equal to 5.14, and the calculated value of F also was equal to 5.14, then

    a. Ho is accepted
    *b. Ho is rejected
    c. Ho is equal to Ha
    d. cannot tell from the above information

57. When doing an ANOVA with one degree of freedom between groups, then

    a. only one sample group has been selected
    *b. exactly two sample groups have been selected
    c. more than two sample groups have been selected
    d. cannot tell without knowing the within degrees of freedom

58. An F ratio which equals exactly 1.00, indicates that

    a. the total degrees of freedom are equal to 1
    b. the between degrees of freedom are equal to 1
    c. the within degrees of freedom are equal to 1
    *d. the MS between has exactly the same value as the MS within

59. In order to calculate an F ratio, there must be

    a. more than one sample group
    b. interval data
    c. homogeneous variances among the sample groups
    *d. all of these

60. The factorial ANOVA is only applied when

    *a. there is more than one independent variable
    b. there is more than one dependent variable
    c. there is exactly one independent variable
    d. there is 1 degree of freedom between groups

61. When doing a factorial ANOVA, the main effects are found from the

    a. rows
    b. columns
    *c. both of these
    d. neither of these

62. A factorial ANOVA must have a minimum of

    a. two cells
    *b. four cells
    c. eight cells
    d. none of these, since the factorial ANOVA may be performed on any number of cells

63. On a factorial ANOVA, the number of different variations in treatment conditions, determines the number of

   *a. cells
    b. dependent variables
    c. subjects within each group
    d. all of these

64. A factorial ANOVA may show the significance of

    a. treatment A
    b. treatment B
    c. the interaction between A and B
   *d. all of these

65. On a factorial ANOVA, a significant interaction indicates

   *a. the cumulative effect of two or more independent variables
    b. the partial effect of several independent variables taken separately
    c. the interactive effect of several dependent variables
    d. none of these

66. When several independent variables are manipulated simultaneously, an appropriate analysis would be the

    a. one-way ANOVA
   *b. factorial ANOVA
    c. partial ANOVA
    d. none of these

67. In a factorial ANOVA, the row variability, column variability and rxc variability, are all components of the

    a. MS within
    b. MS total
   *c. MS between
    d. interaction effect

68. In order to calculate an F ratio, there must be

    a. interval data
    b. a normal distribution in the population from which the samples were selected
    c. similarity among the within variances for each sample
   *d. all of these

69. When the data form is nominal, the appropriate F ratio is

    a. the one-way
    b. the two-way
    c. the factorial
   *d. none of these, since F cannot be calculated from nominal data

B. <u>True or False</u>: For the following, indicate T (True) or F (False)

70. The F ratio may compare two or more sample means.   T

71. The F ratio may only be calculated when the independent variable
    has exactly two levels.   F

72. The F ratio, like the t ratio, can be used to predict the direc-
    tion of the mean difference.   F

73. The F ratio cannot be used on post-facto research data.   F

74. Total variability results from the accumulated differences be-
    tween each individual score and the total mean.   T

75. The variance, or mean square, results from dividing the SS by
    the degrees of freedom.   T

76. Between variability results from the accumulated differences
    between each sample mean and the total mean.   T

77. Within variability results from the accumulated differences
    between each individual score and the total mean.   F

78. The between SS plus the within SS equals the total SS.   T

79. A significant F ratio can only occur when the between variability
    is less than the within variability.   F

80. An ANOVA cannot be done unless the sample sizes are equal.   F

81. When an F ratio is significant, the null hypothesis is accepted.   F

82. An F ratio of 10 means that the MS within is 10 times larger
    than the MS between.   F

83. With a sample mean of 10, the MS must equal 100.   F

84. The factorial ANOVA may not be used unless there is more than   T
    one independent variable.

85. A within MS of zero, indicates that all the sample scores   T
    were identical.

C. For the following questions, calculate the values.

86. Calculate the F ratio on the following sets of scores.

    Group 1   Group 2   Group 3

       4   6   7
       3   3   5
       1   2   1

Ans. .40

87. Calculate the F ratio on the following sets of scores.

Group 1	Group 2	Group 3
5	7	10
3	6	10
3	6	9
2	4	10

Ans. 37.72

88. Calculate the F ratio on the following sets of scores.

Group 1	Group 2	Group 3
5	8	10
4	6	10
1	6	12
1	5	8

Ans. 18.58

89. Calculate the F ratio on the following sets of scores.

Group 1	Group 2	Group 3
6	6	11
4	9	5
3	8	14
1	7	10

Ans. 6.45

90. For the following scores,

Group 1	Group 2	Group 3
5	4	3
3	1	1
1	3	1
3	2	2

a. Calculate the F ratio
b. Should Ho be rejected or accepted? If rejected, state the probability of alpha error.

Ans. a. .91
     b. Accept Ho

91. Three groups of subjects were randomly selected, four subjects in each group. The SS between was 132.17, and the SS within was 19.50.

a. Calculate the F ratio
b. Should Ho be rejected or accepted. If rejected, state the probability of alpha error.

Ans. a. 30.46
     b. Reject Ho. Significant at $P < .01$

92. Three groups of subjects were randomly selected, 10 subjects in each group. The SS between was 668.47, and the SS within was 923.40.

    a. Calculate the F ratio
    b. Should Ho be rejected or accepted? If rejected, state the probability of alpha error.

  Ans. a. 9.77
        b. Reject Ho. Significant at $P < .01$

93. Four groups of subjects were randomly selected, and subjected to different experimental treatments. Their scores were:

Group 1	Group 2	Group 3	Group 4
5	7	8	15
4	5	7	14
3	6	6	18
6	8	8	12

    a. Calculate the F ratio
    b. Should Ho be rejected or accepted? If rejected, state the probability of alpha error.

  Ans. a. 30.61
        b. Reject Ho. Significant at $P < .01$

94. Using the data from question # 93, and if appropriate, calculate an HSD, setting alpha at .05.

    a. Calculate the HSD
    b. Indicate which means differ significantly

  Ans. a. 3.40
        b. Means 1, 2, 3 do not differ, but all differ significantly from Mean 4.

95. Three groups of subjects were randomly selected, and subjected to different experimental treatments. Their scores were:

Group 1	Group 2	Group 3
10	15	20
12	17	17
9	10	19
10	15	18
9	16	25
5	14	16
8	13	15

    a. Calculate the F ratio
    b. Should Ho be rejected or accepted? If rejected, state the probability of alpha error.

  Ans. a. 23.15
        b. Reject Ho. Significant at $P < .01$

96. Using the data from question #95, and if appropriate, set alpha at .05 and calculate an HSD

    a. Calculate the HSD
    b. Indicate which means differ significantly

    Ans. a. 3.57
         b. All these means differ significantly from each other.

97. On the following four-cell design:

a	10	b	14
	8		15
	8		12
	9		13
c	4	d	7
	3		9
	3		6
	6		7

Calculate a factorial ANOVA.
Indicate for each component both the statistical decision and the alpha error.

Ans. F for rows = 78.57 Reject Ho. Significant at $P < .01$
     F for columns = 41.56 Reject Ho. Significant at $P < .01$
     F for interactions = 1.46 Accept Ho. Not significant

98. On the following four-cell design:

a	12	b	7
	10		10
	10		10
c	5	d	3
	6		4
	8		2

Calculate a factorial ANOVA. Indicate for each component both the statistical decision and the alpha error.

Ans. F for rows = 41.71 Reject Ho. Significant at $P < .01$
     F for columns = 9.77 Reject Ho. Significant at $P < .05$
     F for interaction = 1.09 Accept Ho. Not significant

99. On the following four-cell design:

a	3	b	7
	3		6
	2		6
	1		4
c	5	d	11
	5		10
	3		9
	4		8

Calculate a factorial ANOVA
Indicate for each component both the statistical decision and the alpha error.

Ans. F for rows = 26.04 Reject Ho. Significant at $P < .01$
     F for columns = 60.29 Reject Ho. Significant at $P < .01$
     F for interaction = 2.40 Accept Ho. Not significant

100. On the following four-cell design:

a	5	b	7
	6		8
	4		9
	3		7

Calculate a factorial ANOVA. Indicate for each component both the statistical decision and the alpha error.

c	10	d	12
	10		10
	9		12
	10		12

Ans. F for rows = 83.39 Reject Ho. Significant at $P < .01$
F for columns = 26.05 Reject Ho. Significant at $P < .01$
F for interaction = 2.32 Accept Ho. Not significant

For questions 101 through 109 use the following data:

A researcher is interested in establishing whether memory is a function of both IQ and time of testing. A random sample of 40 university students was selected and each student was given an IQ test. Half of the students scored above 115 and were assigned to the high IQ category, while the others were assigned to the average IQ category. The students were than all given a series of paragraphs to read, followed by a memory test on the content of what had been read. Half the students took the memory test immediately after reading the material, while the other half waited one hour before testing. The results were as follows (high scores indicating better memory retention):

TIME OF TESTING

		DELAY	IMMEDIATE
	a	3.0	b 6.5
		4.1	5.3
		3.6	7.1
		3.8	6.7
AVERAGE		5.0	5.8
		4.3	6.1
		3.3	7.0
		2.9	5.5
		4.5	6.2
		4.2	6.6
IQ			
	c	5.2	d 7.3
		5.4	7.1
		5.1	8.2
		7.0	7.9
HIGH		6.8	8.5
		5.7	7.9
		6.1	7.8
		4.9	8.5
		5.2	8.8
		4.6	7.0

101. Find the MS within.

Ans. .46

102. Find the MS for rows.

Ans. 28.05

103. Find the MS for columns.

Ans. 55.45

104. Find the MS for interaction.

Ans. .04

105. Find the F ratio for rows, and if significant, state the alpha error.

Ans. F for rows = 60.98 Reject Ho. Significant at $P < .01$

106. Find the F ratio for columns, and if significant, state the alpha error.

Ans. F for columns = 120.54 Reject Ho. Significant at $P < .01$

107. Find the F ratio for the interaction, and if significant, state the alpha error.

Ans. F for interaction = .09 Accept Ho. Not significant

108. Was the row independent variable manipulated or assigned?

Ans. Subjects were assigned to the rows on the basis of IQ scores.

109. Was the column independent variable manipulated or assigned?

Ans. The columns, time of testing, contained a manipulated independent variable.

A. Multiple Choice Items

1. When measuring individuals with the nominal scale, the key question is,

   a. how much of the given trait does the individual possess?
   b. does individual A possess more of the given trait than individual B?
   *c. does the individual possess or not possess the trait?
   d. all of these are key questions when using the nominal scale

2. All nominal categories

   a. must share a given trait
   b. must overlap
   *c. must be totally independent of each other
   d. must be rank-ordered

3. When using the nominal scale to assess political-party affiliation,

   a. the strength of each individual's party loyalty must be established
   b. the subjects within each category must be rank-ordered with respect to affiliative strength
   c. each and every subject must receive a different scale number
   *d. the individuals must be grouped as to party preference

4. The major mathematical rule underlying nominal scaling is

   a. the greater-than, or less-than rule
   *b. the equality versus non-equality rule
   c. the equal-appearing-intervals rule
   d. none of these, since nominal scaling is not mathematical

5. If, during a recent presidential campaign, a certain random sample of voters indicated 30 persons for Reagan, 25 for Mondale, and 10 for "others", the resulting scale would be

   *a. nominal
   b. ordinal
   c. interval
   d. ratio

6. If a certain nominal scale, applied to a single group of subjects, showed observed frequencies of 30, 25 and 20, the frequencies expected on the basis of chance would be

   a. 30, 25 and 20
   b. 30, 30 and 25
   c. 25, 30 and 25
   *d. 25, 25 and 25

7. When a single group of subjects is allocated among any number of categories, the chi square analysis is

   a. r by k
   b. r by 1
   c. 2 by 2
   *d. 1 by k

8. When a single group of subjects is allocated among any number of categories, the chance fe's for the chi square are

   a. equal to the size of the sample
 *b. equal to the fo's, divided by the sample size
   c. equal to the sample size, divided by the fo's
   d. equal to the fo's

9. The null hypothesis for chi square states that the

   a. means for each group are equal
   b. means for each group are equal to the fo's
 *c. fo's are equal to the fe's
   d. population mean is equal to the sample mean

10. For any chi square, the degrees of freedom are equal to

   a. the size of the sample
   b. sample size, minus 1
   c. sample size, minus 2
 *d. none of these

11. When the chi square fo's deviate significantly from the fe's, then

   a. the independent rule has been violated
   b. the data are not nominal
   c. the chi square cannot be calculated
 *d. null is rejected

12. With chi square, the more categories there are

   a. the fewer the degrees of freedom
 *b. the greater the degrees of freedom
   c. the higher the fo values
   d. the higher the fe values

13. With chi square, when an apriori hypothesis is tested

   a. the fe's must equal the fo's
   b. the fe's must all equal each other
   c. no single fe may ever equal a given fo
 *d. none of these

14. When the fe's are determined, not on the basis of strict chance, but on some previous theory, then the tested hypothesis is

   a. accepted
   b. rejected
   c. no longer appropriate to a chi square analysis
 *d. apriori

15. When the obtained value of chi square is equal to the critical, table value for a given number of degrees of freedom, then

 *a. Ho is rejected
   b. Ho is accepted
   c. the alternate hypothesis is accepted
   d. none of these, since no conclusions are possible when the obtained value equals the tabled value

16. On a 1 by k chi square with a sample size of 100, the degrees of freedom must **always** equal

    a. 100
    b. 99
    *c. k-1
    d. none of these

17. The degrees of freedom for a 2 by 2 chi square must **always** equal

    a. 4
    b. 2
    *c. 1
    d. none of these

18. On a 1 by k chi square, the tabled value needed for significance, at a given alpha level, cannot be found unless

    a. the number of subjects is known
    *b. the number of categories is known
    c. the number of rows is known
    d. all of these

19. When the chi square value is negative, it means

    a. the relationship is inverse
    b. the second group is higher than the first group
    c. the fo's are greater than the fe's
    *d. none of these, since obtaining a negative chi square is impossible

20. The degrees of freedom on a 3 by 3 chi square are equal to

    a. 9
    *b. 4
    c. 3
    d. cannot tell from the above information

21. A researcher obtains a 2 by 2 chi square value of 3.83. The appropriate degrees of freedom indicate required table values of 3.84 at .05, and 6.64 at .01. The researcher should

    *a. accept Ho
    b. reject Ho at .05
    c. reject Ho at .01
    d. only test the apriori hypothesis

22. Whenever a single group of subjects is being allocated among four independent categories, the chi square analysis would be

    a. 1 by 3
    *b. 1 by 4
    c. 2 by 2
    d. cannot tell from the above information

23. In the chi square table of critical values, as degrees of freedom increase

    *a. so too do the critical values
    b. the critical values decrease

c. the critical values remain constant
d. none of these, since for chi square the critical table values
    are independent of the degrees of freedom

24. When several groups of subjects are being compared with regard to
    some observed frequencies, the appropriate chi square analysis would be

    a. 1 by k
    *b. r by k
    c. N by df
    d. none of these

25. When fe's are obtained by multiplying row totals by column totals, and
    then divided by N, the chi square is a (n)

    a. 1 by k
    *b. r by k
    c. 1 by r
    d. all of these, depending on the degrees of freedom

26. When comparing two or more groups with regard to some observed frequencies,
    the independent variable must be set in the

    *a. rows
    b. columns
    c. marginal totals
    d. lower, right-hand corner

27. When comparing two or more groups with regard to some observed
    frequencies, the dependent variable must by set in the

    a. rows
    *b. columns
    c. marginal totals
    d. lower, right-hand corner

28. When doing a 2 by 2 chi square, when any expected frequency is less than
    10,

    a. the chi square should not be calculated
    *b. reduce the fo-fe value by .5
    c. increase the fe by .5
    d. reduce the fe by .5

29. The Yates correction may only be applied

    a. when any fo is less than 5
    b. when any fo is less than fe
    c. when chi square equals 0
    *d. none of these

30. Regardless of the fo or fe values, the Yates correction need only be
    applied when

    a. the chi square is significant
    b. the difference between a given fo and fe is less than 10
    *c. the df equals 1
    d. none of these

31. The effect of the Yates correction on the chi square value is that chi square is

   *a. slightly decreased
    b. slightly increased
    c. greatly increased
    d. none of these, since Yates does not influence the chi square value

32. When Yates is applied, the likelihood of obtaining a significant chi square is

   *a. slightly decreased
    b. slightly increased
    c. greatly increased
    d. eliminated

Questions 33 through 42 are based on the following:

   A researcher randomly selects two sample groups and provides one group with daily doses of vitamin C and the other group with a placebo. Later, the two groups are compared as to whether or not the subjects caught the flu.

33. The measurement scale employed in the study was

   *a. nominal
    b. ordinal
    c. interval
    d. ratio

34. The independent variable in the study was

    a. whether or not the subjects caught the flu
   *b. whether or not the subjects received the vitamin C
    c. the control group
    d. the placebo

35. The dependent variable in the study was

   *a. whether or not the subjects caught the flu
    b. whether or not the subjects received the vitamin C
    c. the control group
    d. the placebo

36. This is an example of

    a. post-facto research
   *b. experimental research
    c. correlational research
    d. none of these

37. The independent variable in this study was

    a. assigned
    b. not allowed to vary
   *c. manipulated
    d. significant

38. The appropriate analysis of these data would involve

    a. a 1 by k chi square
    b. a 1 by r chi square
  *c. a 2 by 2 chi square
    d. Cramer's V, followed by a chi square

39. In setting up the contingency table, whether or not the groups received the vitamin C should be placed in the

    a. columns
  *b. rows
    c. marginal totals
    d. lower, right-hand corner

40. In setting up the contingency table, whether or not the groups caught the flu should be placed in the

  *a. columns
    b. rows
    c. marginal totals
    d. lower, right-hand corner

41. In evaluating these data, the chi square's degrees of freedom would equal

  *a. 1
    b. 4
    c. 2
    d. cannot tell from the information provided

42. In analyzing the data from this research, the Yates correction should only be applied if

    a. one or more of the fo's was less than 10
    b. one or more of the fo's was greater than 10
  *c. one or more of the fe's was less than 10
    d. none of these

43. In order to use the chi square

    a. all **data must** be in nominal form
    b. the categories must be independent of each other
    c. the sum total of all fo's must equal N
  *d. all of these

44. The chi square statistical test may handle data from

    a. experimental research
    b. post-facto research
  *c. both of these
    d. neither of these

45. Chi square, like t and F, always tests the hypothesis of

    a. association
    b. correlation
  *c. difference
    d. apriori events

46. With chi square, the larger the sample size

    a.   the smaller the alpha error
    b.   the larger the alpha error
    c.   the larger the critical, tabled value needed for significance
    *d. none of these

47. The use of (C), the correlational technique cited in the text for
    nominal data, first requires

    a.   a manipulated independent variable
    b.   an apriori hypothesis
    c.   that the constant, .50, be subtracted from the chi square
    *d. that the chi square be significant

48. The coefficient of contingency (C) may be applied when

    a.   using a 2 by 2 contingency table
    b.   using a 3 by 4 contingency table
    *c. both of these
    d.   neither of these

49. The McNemar test may be used on nominal data taken from

    a.   a before-after design
    b.   a matched- subjects design
    *c. both of these
    d.   neither of these

50. In order to use the McNemar test, the samples should be

    a.   independent of each other
    *b. correlated with each other
    c.   free of sampling error
    d.   normally distributed

51. In order to calculate a chi square, it is assumed that

    a.   the underlying distributions are normal
    b.   the population mean is a known value
    c.   the mean of the sample does not deviate significantly from the
         population mean
    *d. none of these

52. The chi square is a

    a.   parametric test of mean differences
    *b. a non-parametric test of frequency differences
    c.   a parametric test of frequency differences
    d.   an interval test of rank differences

53. Whenever the chi square is applied to interval data, the resulting value
    will be

    a.   inflated
    b.   lowered
    c.   the same as when applied to nominal data
    *d. none of these, since chi square may only be applied to nominal data

54. The McNemar test may only be used when the contingency table is

    a. 1 by k
 *b. 2 by 2
    c. 2 by 3
    d. none of these, since the McNemar test may be applied to contingency tables of any size

55. The chi square test may not be used when

    a. the underlying distributions are skewed
    b. the variability within the sample differs
    c. the intervals between successive scale points are not equal
 *d. none of these

56. When the 2 by 2 chi square contingency table contains expected frequencies of less than 5,

    a. the Yates correction must be applied
    b. coefficient of contingency must be applied
    c. the degrees of freedom then must increase by 5
 *d. the chi square should not be calculated

57. When using chi square, the larger the alpha error

    a. the more difficult it becomes to reject Ho
 *b. the easier it becomes to reject Ho
    c. the greater the degrees of freedom
    d. none of these

B. <u>True of False</u>: For the following, indicate T (True) or F (False)

58. Chi square is a non-parametric statistical test.   T

59. Chi square may never be used with nominal data.   F

60. The null hypothesis for chi square states that the observed   T
    frequencies are equal to the expected frequencies.

61. The degrees of freedom for chi square are based on the   F
    sample size.

62. Chi square may not be used when comparing two or more   F
    samples.

63. When any expected frequency is less than 10, Yates should   T
    be applied (when df= 1).

64. Every 2 by 2 chi square, regardless of sample size, contains   T
    only 1 degree of freedom.

65. Unlike t or F, as the degrees of freedom increase for chi   T
    square, the critical, table values also increase.

66. When applying chi square to a 2 by 2 contingency table, each   F
    fo must be <u>at</u> <u>least</u> equal to 10.

67. When applying chi square to a 3 by 5 contingency table,   F
    Yates must be used whenever any fe is less than 10.

68. Because of the independence restriction, the McNemar test cannot be used on correlated samples. F

69. As long as the data are in nominal form, the McNemar test may be applied to matched-subjects design results. T

70. When chi square equals zero, Ho must be accepted. T

71. In order to use chi square, the underlying distribution must be normal. F

72. Applying the Yates correction, makes it somewhat easier to accept Ho. T

73. Other things being equal, the larger the chi square value, the greater the likelihood of rejecting Ho. T

74. The Yates correction is designed to <u>reduce</u> the value of chi square. T

75. In a 1 by k chi square, the expected frequency is always equal to k-1. F

76. The chi square test demands that cell entries be independent of each other. T

77. Chi square may only be used to compare frequencies, never sample means. T

78. When analyzing research data via the chi square, the independent variable should be placed in the rows. T

79. Chi square may only be used for the analysis of post-facto research data. F

80. Correlations may never be established when the data form is nominal. F

81. The coefficient of contingency (C) demands that there be <u>only</u> 4 independent cells. F

82. Chi square is a far more powerful test than is either t of F. F

83. If one group of 35 subjects is being sorted into 8 independent categories, the chi square <u>must</u> have 7 degrees of freedom. T

C. For the following questions, calculate the values.

84. Calculate the chi square on the following nominal data.

CATEGORIES

	A	B	C	D	E
fo	30	20	20	15	15

Ans. 7.50

85. Calculate a chi square on the following nominal data.

CATEGORIES

	A	B	C
fo	35	25	10

Ans. 13.58

86. Calculate a chi square on the following nominal data.

CATEGORIES

	A	B	C	D
fo	30	10	20	20

Ans. 10.00

87. Calculate a chi square on the following nominal data.

CATEGORIES

	A	B	C	D
fo	10	20	15	15

Ans. 3.34

88. On the following nominal data,

CATEGORIES

	A	B	C
fo	35	15	10

a. Calculate the chi square.
b. Should Ho be rejected or accepted? If rejected, state the alpha error.

Ans. a. 17.50
b. Reject Ho. Significant at $P < .01$

89. On the following nominal data,

CATEGORIES

	A	B	C	D	E
fo	40	20	20	10	10

a. Calculate the chi square.
b. Should Ho be rejected or accepted? If rejected, state the alpha error.

Ans. a. 30
b. Reject Ho. Significant at $P < .01$

90. On the following data,

CATEGORIES

	A	B	C	D
fo	19	21	18	22

a. Calculate the chi square
b. Should Ho be rejected or accepted? If rejected, state the alpha error.

Ans. a. .50
      b. Accept Ho. Not significant.

For questions 91 through 96, use the following:

Hypothesis: Police citations for traffic violations are a function of the age of the driver. A random sample of 50 drivers was selected from the population of cited traffic violators during a one-month period. The drivers were categorized according to age, and the frequencies for each category were established.

AGE OF DRIVER

	18-27	28-37	38-47	48-57	58 and over
fo	35	25	15	13	12

91. Calculate the chi square.

Ans. 19.40

92. Indicate the number of degrees of freedom.

Ans. 4

93. Indicate the tabled value for chi square at the .05 level.

Ans. 9.49

94. Indicate the tabled value for chi square at the .01 level.

Ans. 13.28

95. Should Ho be rejected or accepted?

Ans. Rejected

96. State the probability value of the alpha error.

Ans. $P < .01$

97. Using the nominal data in the following contingency table:

a	b
40	20
c	d
10	20

a. Calculate the chi square.
b. Should Ho be rejected or accepted? If rejected, state the alpha error.

Ans. a. 9.01
      b. Reject Ho. Significant at $P < .01$

98. Using the nominal data in the following contingency table:

a	b
30	10
c	d
20	20

    a. Calculate the chi square.
    b. Should Ho be rejected or accepted?
       If rejected, state the alpha error.

Ans. a. 5.34
      b. Reject Ho. Significant at $P < .05$

99. Using the nominal data in the following table:

a	b
30	5
c	d
5	10

    a. If appropriate, calculate the chi square.
    b. Should Ho be rejected or accepted?
       If rejected, state the alpha error.

Ans. a. Chi square not appropriate, since the fe for cell "d" is
        less than 5.
      b. Ho can neither be rejected or accepted.

100. Using the nominal data in the following table:

a	b
15	10
c	d
10	15

    a. If appropriate, calculate the chi square.
    b. Should Ho be rejected or accepted?
       If rejected, state the alpha error.

Ans. a. 2.00
      b. Ho accepted. Not significant.

101. Hypothesis: There is a correlation between hair color and eye color.
A random sample of 90 college students was selected, 60 brunettes and
30 blondes. Of the brunettes 40 had brown eyes, and 20 had blue eyes.
of the blondes, 10 had brown eyes and 20 had blue eyes.

If appropriate, test the hypothesis using the coefficient of contingency.

Ans. Since the chi square value of 9.01 was significant, C is
     appropriate and equals .30.

102. On the following nominal data:

a	b
7	13
c	d
15	5

    a. Calculate the chi square.
    b. Should Ho be rejected or accepted?
       If rejected, state the alpha error.

Ans. a. Using the Yates correction, chi square is equal to 4.94.
      b. Reject Ho. Significant at $P < .05$

103. On the following nominal data:

a	b
10	5
c	d
4	11

    a. Calculate the chi square.
    b. Should Ho be rejected or accepted?
       If rejected, state the alpha error.

Ans. Using the Yates correction, chi square equals 3.34.
     b. Accept Ho. Not significant

104. On the following nominal data:

a	b
15	10
c	d
12	12
e	f
10	10

    a. Calculate the chi square.
    b. If appropriate, calculate C (the coefficient of contingency).

Ans. a. .65
     b. Not appropriate to calculate C, since chi square is not significant.

105. On the following nominal data:

a	b
14	8
c	d
12	13
e	f
12	9

    a. Calculate the chi square.
    b. If appropriate, calculate C (the coefficient of contingency).

Ans. a. 1.19
     b. Ho accepted. Not significant

106. A researcher does a 3 by 3 chi square, and finds a significant value of 13.29. The sample size is 50. Calculate C (the coefficient of contingency).

Ans. .46

107. A researcher does a 3 by 4 chi square, and finds a significant value of 17.50. The sample size is 25. Calculate C (the coefficient of contingency).

Ans. .64

A. Multiple Choice Items

1. The major goal of correlational research is to

    a. establish cause-and-effect relationships
    b. analyze the effects of an actively manipulated independent variable
    c. evaluate the results of experimental research
    *d. make better-than-chance predictions

2. The higher the correlation between X and Y, then

    a. the higher the probability of having isolated the causal factor
    b. the higher the probability of having sampled from a single population
    c. the higher the probability of inflating the alpha error
    *d. the more accurate the resulting predictions

3. The regression of Y on X allows for

    *a. predictions of Y, given information on X
    b. predictions of X, given information on X, Y and Z
    c. predictions of both X and Y, given information on a third variable
    d. none of these

4. The regression line

    a. is drawn through the points on a scatter plot
    b. is a straight line
    c. comes closest to the majority of the scatter points
    *d. all of these

5. The regression equation of Y on X

    *a. produces a straight line
    b. produces a curvilinear relationship
    c. always slopes from upper left to lower right
    d. all of these

6. In order to produce the regression line, the researcher must know

    a. how much the scatter points deviate from the line
    b. the slope of the line
    c. where the line crosses the ordinate
    *d. all of these

7. In the regression equation for Y on X, the "a" term symbolizes

    a. the slope of the line
    b. the amount of scatter around the line
    *c. the point of intercept
    d. the correlation coefficient

8. The slope of the regression line is designated as

    a. a   c. y
    *b. b   d. r

9. The regression line's point of intercept designates

    a. the slope of the line
    b. the amount of change in Y which accompanies a given change in X
  *c. the value of Y when X is equal to zero
    d. the strength of the correlation

10. In regression analysis, the amount of change in Y which accompanies a given change in X is designated by

  *a. the slope of the regression line
    b. the Y intercept
    c. the "a" value
    d. the magnitude of the difference between X and Y

11. The higher the correlation between X and Y

    a. the more the scatter points deviate from the regression line
  *b. the more the scatter points cluster around the regression line
    c. the more the scatter points create a circular configuration
    d. none of these

12. In regression analysis, when Y increases by two units for each equal single-unit increase in X, then

    a. the intercept equals +2.00
    b. the intercept equals +.50
  *c the slope equals +2.00
    d. the slope equals +.50

13. The slope of the regression line

    a.. may never be negative
    b. may never be greater than +1.00
    c. may never be greater than the correlation value
  *d. none of these

14. When high scores on X associate with low scores on Y, the regression line

  *a. has a negative slope
    b. crosses the ordinate at the zero point
    c. runs parallel to the abscissa
    d. runs parallel to the ordinate

15. Whenever the correlation has a positive value, so too will the

  *a. slope of the regression line be positive
    b. Y intercept be positive
    c. mean of the Y distribution
    d. mean of the X distribution be positive

16. Whenever the value of the correlation is negative

    a. the resulting predictions will be inaccurate
    b. the amount of information about Y being contained in X is zero
    c. both of these
  *d. neither of these

17. When Y decreases by one unit for each equal unit increase in X, then

    a. the intercept value will be negative
  *b. the slope value will be negative
    c. the correlation value will be positive
    d. both a and b, but not c

18. The higher the value of the Y intercept

    a. the higher the correlation value
    b. the higher the slope value
    c. the higher the value of the mean of X
  *d. none of these

19. When the correlation between X and Y is zero, then the safest prediction of Y which can be made, given information on X,

    a. is the mean of X
  *b. is the mean of Y
    c. is the mean of the combined distributions of X and Y
    d. none of these

20. When the correlation between X and Y is equal to zero, then the only possible value that the Y pred. may take on is

    a. zero
    b. a value equal to the slope
    c. a value equal to $\overline{X}$
  *d. a value equal to $\overline{Y}$

21. When the standard deviations of both the X and Y distributions are equal, then

  *a. the value of the slope equals the value of the correlation
    b. the value of the Y intercept equals $\overline{Y}$
    c. the value of $\overline{X}$ equals the value of $\overline{Y}$
    d. none of these

22. When the correlation between X and Y equals zero, then the slope of the regression line of Y on X is equal to

    a. the mean of Y
    b. the point of intercept
  *c. zero
    d. none of these

23. When the standard deviation of the Y distribution equals zero, then

  *a. the slope of the regression line of Y on X equals zero
    b. the mean of X equals zero
    c. the mean of Y equals zero
    d. none of these

24. The higher the correlation between X and Y, then

    a. the more likely it is to be positive
    b. the less likely that null will be rejected
    c. the less the predicted value of Y may deviate from the mean of Y
  *d. the more the predicted value of Y may deviate from the mean of Y

25. The discovery of the regression phenomenon is credited to

    a. Karl Pearson
    *b. Sir Francis Galton
    c. Sir Ronald Fisher
    d. Dr. Sigmund Gestalt

26. According to the regression concept, the children of very tall parents

    *a. should be taller than average, but shorter than their parents
    b. should be at least as tall as their parents
    c. should be below average in height
    d. should just as likely be tall as short

27. The lower the value of the correlation between X and Y, the more the predicted Y values

    *a. will regress toward the mean of Y
    b. will deviate from the mean of Y
    c. will assume a mean of zero
    d. both b and c, but not a

28. Whenever the calculated value of r equals the critical, tabled value of r for a given number of degrees of freedom, then

    a. Ho is accepted
    *b. Ho is rejected
    c. the mean of Z equals the mean of Y
    d. the alpha error is rejected

29. When the correlation in a sample is found to be significant, then it is assumed that

    a. the mean of Y differs from the mean of X in the population
    b. the mean of Y equals the mean of X in the population
    c. the regression of Y on X cannot be determined
    *d. the correlation also exists in the population

30. Secular trend analysis refers to data on the distribution which are

    *a. spread out over time
    b. non-significant
    c. significant
    d. none of these

31. The use of historical data to predict trends over time is called

    a. the regression asymptote
    b. kurtosis
    c. the Spearman trendex
    *d. secular trend analysis

32. When the correlation between X and Y equals zero, the standard error of estimate

    a. equals 0
    b. equals the mean of Y
    *c. equals the standard deviation of Y
    d. equals 1.00

33. When the correlation between X and Y equals 1.00, the standard error of estimate

   *a. equals 0
    b. equals the mean of Y
    c. equals the standard deviation of Y
    d. equals 1.00

34. The value of the standard error of estimate may never be greater than

    a. 1.00
    b. 0
    c. the mean of Y
   *d. the standard deviation of Y

35. The value of the standard error of estimate may never be less than

    a. 1.00
   *b. 0
    c. the mean of Y
    d. the standard deviation of Y

36. The most accurate predictions are made when the standard error of estimate equals

    a. 1.00
   *b. 0
    c. the mean of Y
    d. the standard deviation of Y

37. When using the standard error of estimate for establishing the confidence interval at .95, then z scores of

    a. +1.00 should be used
   *b. +1.96 should be used
    c. +.05 should be used
    d, +.95 should be used

38. When using the standard error of estimate for establishing a confidence interval of .99, then one should use z scores of

    a. +1.00
    b. +.01
    c. +.99
   *d. +2.58

39. When the slope of the regression line equals -3.00, then

    a. the Y intercept equals -3.00
    b. there is a 3 equal-unit gain in Y for each unit gain in X
   *c. there is a 3 equal-unit loss in Y for each unit gain in X
    d. there is a one-third, equal-unit loss in Y for each unit gain in X

40. When the Y intercept equals +1.00, then

    a. the correlation between X and Y equals +1.00
    b. the slope of the regression line equals +1.00
    c. an X score of +1.00 corresponds with a Y score of 0
   *d. a Y score of +1.00 corresponds with an X score of 0

41. When a correlation value among three or more interval-data variables is required, then the appropriate statistical test is

    *a. the multiple R
    b. the Pearson r
    c. the Spearman r_s
    d. the multi-factor V

42. In order to use the multiple R,

    *a. all the internal correlations must be significant
    b. at least four variables must be involved
    c. the correlation between r and r_s must be significant
    d. Ho must be accepted

43. When information regarding two or more variables is combined in order to predict performance, then the appropriate statistical test is

    a. the partial correlation
    b. the Galton "g"
    c. the Yates Correction
    *d. the multiple R

44. When the slope of the regression line of Y on X is positive, then the array of data points on the scatter plot

    a. goes from upper left to lower right
    *b. goes from lower left to upper right
    c. goes parallel to the abscissa
    d. none of these

45. The most efficient use of the multiple R is when

    *a. its value is higher than any of the values of the separate, internal correlations
    b. its value is lower than the values of the separate, internal correlations
    c. the scores to be predicted are in nominal form
    d. the research is experimental

46. In order to utilize the multiple R in making specific Y predictions

    a. the scores must be in interval form
    b. at least two slope values must be determined
    c. Ho must be rejected for each of the internal r's
    *d. all of these

47. When predicting from a three-factor, multiple R, the value of b_1 indicates

    a. the first intercept
    b. the criterion variable
    c. the first predictor variable
    *d. how much change in Y will occur for a given change in the first predictor, when the effects of the second predictor have been held constant

48. The technique employed for establishing the correlation between two variables, when both are known to be correlated with a third variable, is called the

   a. multiple R
   b. coefficient of determination
   c. product-moment
   *d. partial correlation

49. The value for $r_{y1.2}$ provides information regarding

   a. the multiple correlation among three variables
   b. the correlation between variables 1 and 2, with variable Y held constant
   *c. the correlation between variables Y and 1, with variable 2 held constant
   d. the correlation between variables Y and 2, with variable 1 held constant

50. Establishing a three-variable partial correlation, results in

   a. a multiple R
   b. a third-order partial
   c. a second-order partial
   *d. a first-order partial

51. In a four-variable correlation, when two variables are held constant, while examining the remaining relationship between the other two, the technique is referred to as

   a. a multiple R
   b. a first-order partial
   *c. a higher-order partial
   d. none of these

52. When all the points in a scatter plot lie directly on the regression line of Y on X, then

   a. X has caused Y
   b. the correlation must equal 0
   c. the correlation cannot be calculated
   *d. the correlation must equal ± 1.00

53. The correlation between a criterion variable and two or more predictor variables, is called the

   a. partial correlation of X on Y
   b. partial correlation of Y on X
   c. Pearson r
   *d. multiple R

54. In a two-variable scatter plot, the variable being predicted is placed on the

   a. abscissa
   b. regression line
   *c. ordinate
   d. none of these

55. If a researcher sets up a secular trend analysis to predict corporate profits, the abscissa will represent

   *a. time periods
   b. corporate profits
   c. the correlation values
   d. frequency of occurrence

56. A major difference between the Pearson r and the multiple R is that the multiple R requires the use of

   a. sample data
   b. population data
   c. an accuracy measure
   *d. more than two variables

57. The standard error of multiple estimate may be used when making predictions from

   a. two or more predictor variables
   b. a multiple R
   c. a Pearson r
   *d. a and b, but not c

58. For the Pearson r, the greater the number of degrees of freedom, the greater the likelihood of

   a. obtaining significance
   b. rejecting Ho
   c. the sample correlation also existing in the population
   *d. all of these

B. __True or False:__ For the following, indicate T (True) or F (False)

59. If X correlates .95 with Y, then Y correlates .05 with X.   F

60. The multiple R may be used whenever all of the internal correlations are significant.   T

61. The regression line of Y on X must always slope from lower left to upper right.   F

62. The regression line is the single straight line which passes through most of the data points on a scatter plot.   T

63. The regression of Y on X is used to predict X, given information on a third variable.   F

64. The slope of the regression line of Y on X must always assume a positive value.   F

65. The more the value of a Pearson r deviates from zero, the greater its predictive power.   T

66. The major goal of correlational research is to allow for better-than-chance predictions.   T

67. Each single data point on a scatter plot represents a pair of scores.   T

68. In order to obtain significance for the Pearson r, Ho must be rejected.   T

69. For the Pearson r, rejecting Ho means that the obtained correlation does exist in the population.   T

70. In the regression of Y on X, when the Pearson r equals 1.00, so too must the slope value equal 1.00.   F

71. If the Y intercept equals 50, then a Y value of 50 corresponds with an X value of 0.   T

72. If the slope value equals +10, then Y increases by 10 units for each equal unit increase in X.   T

73. When the correlation in the sample is negative, it can never be used to extrapolate to the population.   F

74. The standard error of estimate may never assume a negative value.   T

75. When the standard error of estimate equals zero, it means that all the data points lie right on the regressionline.   T

76. The standard error of estimate may never equal zero, unless the Pearson r equals 1.00.   T

77. The standard error of estimate may never assume a value larger than the true standard deviation of the Y distribution.   T

78. In order to calculate the standard error of estimate, the value of the Pearson r must be known.   T

79. The partial correlation may never be used, unless more than two variables are involved.   T

80. The multiple R is used to assess the strength of the combined correlations among three or more variables.   T

81. A first-order partial correlation assesses the strength of the relationship between two variables, with the effects of a third variables held constant.   T

82. When all of the internal correlations are significant, then the multiple R must always be significant.   T

83. The resulting correlation between two or more predictor variables and a criterion variable is called the multiple R.   T

84. If X is independent of Y, the safest Y pred., given information about X, is the mean of the Y distribution.   T

85. The lower the value of the Pearson r, the greater the likelihood of the Y pred. falling near the mean of Y.   T

86. The Pearson r, the multiple R, and the coefficient of determination all demand at least interval data.   T

87. For the Pearson r, the degrees of freedom are a direct function of the number of pairs of scores.   T

88. A negative correlation may <u>never</u> be a significant correlation.   F

C. For the following questions, calculate the values.

For questions 89 through 91, use the following:

> Assume a significant XY correlation of .60. The mean of X equals 14.00, and the mean of Y equals 2.00. The true standard deviation of the sample X equals 3.00 and the true standard deviation of Y equals .80.

89. Predict a Y value for a known X value of 10.00.

    Ans. 1.36

90. Calculate the standard error of estimate.

    Ans. .64

91. Find the .95 confidence interval for the predicted Y value.

    Ans. .11 to 2.61

For questions 92 through 95, use the following:

> Assume a significant XY correlation of .90. The mean of X equals 100.00. The mean of Y equals 500.00. The true standard deviation of X equals 10.00. The true standard deviation of Y equals 100.00.

92. Predict a Y value for a known X value of 110.00.

    Ans. 590.00

93. Calculate the standard error of estimate.

    Ans. 44.00

94. Find the .95 confidence interval for the predicted Y value.

    Ans. 503.76 to 676.24

95. Find the .99 confidence interval for the predicted Y value.

    Ans. 476.48 to 703.52

For questions 96 through 99, use the following:

> Assume a significant XY correlation of .85. The mean of X equals 800.00, and the mean of Y equals 20.00. The true standard deviation of X equals 75.00, and the true standard deviation of Y equals 3.70.

96. Predict a Y value for a known X value 1100.00.

    Ans. 32.00

97. Calculate the standard error of estimate.

    Ans. 1.96

98. Find the .95 confidence interval for the predicted Y value.

Ans. 28.16 to 35.84

99. Find the .99 confidence interval for the predicted Y value.

Ans. 26.94 to 37.06

For questions 100 through 105, use the following:

A researcher selects a random sample of 8 high school students. Each student is tested on both Need Achievement and Mechanical Aptitude. The scores were:

Subject	Need Achievement	Mechanical Aptitude
1	12	10
2	2	3
3	5	7
4	9	5
5	11	9
6	10	8
7	4	6
8	1	3

100. Find the Pearson r correlation between Need Achievement and Mechanical Aptitude.

Ans. .87

101. Should Ho be rejected or accepted? and if rejected, state the alpha error.

Ans. Reject Ho. Significant at $P < .01$

102. Predict a Y value for a known X value of 8.00.

Ans. 7.04

103. Find the standard error of estimate.

Ans. 1.20

104. Find the .95 confidence interval for the predicted Y value.

Ans. 4.69 to 9.39

105. Find the .99 confidence interval for the predicted Y value.

Ans. 3.94 to 10.14

For questions 106 through 111, use the following:

A group of 8 elementary school students was randomly selected. Each pupil was tested on both Math Ability and Spelling Ability. Their scores were:

Subject	Math Test	Spelling Test
1	14	15
2	12	10
3	3	2
4	9	10
5	8	7
6	5	6
7	10	9
8	2	4

106. Find the Pearson r correlation between the Math and Spelling scores.

   Ans. .94

107. Should Ho be rejected or accepted? If rejected, state the alpha error.

   Ans. Reject Ho. Significant at $P < .01$.

108. Predict a Y value for a given X value of 7.00.

   Ans. 7.10

109. Find the standard error of estimate.

   Ans. 1.32

110. Find the .95 confidence interval for the predicted Y score.

   Ans. 4.51 to 9.69

111. Find the .99 confidence interval for the predicted Y score.

   Ans. 3.69 to 10.51

112. The Pearson r correlation between variables y and 1 is a significant
   .60. The Pearson r correlation between variables y and 2 is a significant .50. The Pearson r between variables 1 and 2 is a significant
   .70. Find the multiple R for predicting y from 1 and 2.

   Ans. .61

113. The Pearson r between variables y and 1 is a significant .73. The
   Pearson r between variables y and 2 is a significant .79. The Pearson
   r between variables 1 and 2 is a significant .62. Find the multiple R
   for predicting y from 1 and 2.

   Ans. .83

114. A researcher runs Pearson r correlations among three variables, Grade-
   Point Average, IQ and Reading Speed. All correlations are significant.
   GPA and IQ = .80
   GPA and Reading Speed = .85
   IQ and Reading Speed = .60
   Find the multiple R for predicting Grade-Point average from IQ and
   Reading Speed.

   Ans. .92

115. A corporate researcher runs Pearson r correlations among three variables, net income, gross income and amount spent on advertising. All correlations are significant.
Net Income and Gross Income = .60
Net Income and Advertising = .53
Gross Income and Advertising = .35
Find the multiple R for predicting net income from both gross income and advertising.

Ans. .69

For questions 116 through 119, use the following:

A researcher collects the following measures:
$\overline{Y}$ = 50, with a standard deviation of 10
$\overline{X}_1$ = 100, with a standard deviation of 15
$\overline{X}_2$ = 200, with a standard deviation of 20
Significant correlations among the variables were found to be as follows:
y and 1 = .60
y and 2 = .75
1 and 2 = .20

116. Find the multiple R for predicting y from 1 and 2.

Ans. .88

117. Predict the Y value for a known X_1 value of 115 and a known X_2 value of 220.

Ans. 61.25

118. Calculate the standard error of multiple estimate.

Ans. 4.80

119. Find the .99 confidence interval for the predicted Y score.

Ans. 48.87 to 73.63

For questions 120 through 123, use the following:

A random sample of college students was selected from the population of male, physical-education majors. The mean height was 68". The mean weight was 150 lbs. The mean waist-measure size was 32". The standard deviations were,
for height, 3"
for weight, 30 lbs.
for waist-size, 2"
Significant Pearson r's were,
Height and weight, .70
Height and waist-size, .40
Weight and waist-size, .30

120. Find the multiple R for predicting height from both weight and waist-size.

Ans. .73

121. Predict the height of a student whose weight was 120 lbs., and who had a waist-size of 29".

Ans. 65.24"

122. Calculate the standard error of multiple estimate.

Ans. 2.07

123. Find the .95 confidence interval for the predicted Y value.

Ans. 61.18 to 69.30

For questions 124 through 128, use the following:

A given company has corporate profits for the ten-year period 1977 to 1986 of,

YEAR	PROFITS
1977	$ .90
1978	$ 1.10
1979	$ 1.00
1980	$ 1.20
1981	$ 1.40
1982	$ 1.50
1983	$ 1.60
1984	$ 1.90
1985	$ 2.30
1986	$ 2.40

124. What is the Pearson r value?

Ans. .96

125. Should Ho be rejected or accepted? If rejected, state the alpha error.

Ans. Reject Ho. Significant at $P < .01$

126. On the basis of the 10-year trend, how much should the corporation earn in 1989?

Ans. $2.80

127. Find the standard error of estimate.

Ans. .14

128. Find the .95 confidence interval for the predicted earnings in 1989.

Ans. 2.53 to 3.07

129. Among elementary school children, the correlation between strength and weight is .60, and the correlation between strength and age is .70. The correlation between weight and age is .80. (All correlations are significant.) What is the partial correlation between strength and weight, holding age constant?

Ans. .10

130. For a certain major corporation, the correlation between sales and the advertising budget is .50. Between sales and inflation, the correlation is .60. The correlation between inflation and advertising budget is .70. (All correlations are significant). What is the partial correlation between the advertising budget and sales, holding inflation constant?

Ans.   .14

A. Multiple Choice Items

1. Of the following research designs, the one(s) in which the sample scores
   may be independent of each other, is (are) the

   *a. after-only
   b. before-after
   c. matched-subjects
   d. all of these

2. Of the following research designs, the one(s) requiring active manipula-
   tion of the independent variable is (are) the

   a. after-only
   b. before-after
   c. matched-subjects
   *d. all of these

3. Of the following experimental designs, the one(s) in which sample scores
   are correlated with each other is (are) the

   a. after-only
   b. before-after
   c. matched-subjects
   *d. both b and c, but not a

4. When experimental research yields a significant correlation between
   pairs of scores, the experimental design was

   a. either after-only, or before-after
   b. either after-only, or matched-subjects
   *c. either before-after, or matched subjects
   d. all of these

5. When the subjects are measured in the "pre" condition, then the
   independent variable is inserted, and the subjects are measured again
   in the "post" condition, the experimental design is

   a. test-retest
   *b. before-after
   c. post-facto
   d. none of these

6. In comparing the after-only with the matched-subjects designs, the
   matched-subjects design should yield

   *a. a significant positive correlation between the paired scores
   b. no correlation between paired scores
   c. a significant negative correlation between the paired scores
   d. a partial correlation

7. Whenever the before-after design is used

   a. the same subjects are used as their own controls
   b. there should be a positive correlation between the pre and post scores
   c. the researcher is using the post-facto method
   *d. both a and b, but not c

8. The correlated t is to the independent t, as

   a. chi square is to ANOVA
   b. the Pearson r is to the Spearman r_s
   c. the Pearson r is to the chi square
   *d. the before-after design is to the after-only design

9. With interval data and random assignment of subjects, the appropriate analysis of data from an after-only (two group) design would be

   a. the correlated t
   b. the Pearson r
   *c. the independent t
   d. the Spearman r_s

10. The after-only design, with random assignment of subjects, should yield _____ between the scores in the two groups.

    a. a significant positive correlation
    b. a significant negative correlation
    *c. no correlation
    d. all of these, depending on the degrees of freedom

11. For a given number of scores, the independent t has _____ the degrees of freedom as the correlated t.

    a. one-half
    *b. twice
    c. the same
    d. cannot tell from the above information

12. In a correlated t, when the correlation is significant,

    a. the degrees of freedom become less
    b. the alpha error becomes smaller
    c. the estimated standard error of difference is increased
    *d. the estimated standard error of difference is reduced

13. Whenever the value of the estimated standard error of difference is increased, then

    a. the positive correlation was significant
    b. the zero correlation was not significant
    c. the before-after design was used
    *d. none of these

14. With any t test, independent or correlated, the more subjects there are being measured

    *a. the greater the number of degrees of freedom
    b. the fewer the degrees of freedom

c. the greater the alpha error
d. none of these

15. The final goal of the correlated t, is to

   a. test the hypothesis of association
*b. test the hypothesis of difference
   c. match the independent and dependent variables
   d. match the independent and control variables

16. The final goal of the independent t is to

   a. test the hypothesis of association
*b. test the hypothesis of difference
   c. match the independent and dependent variables
   d. match the independent and control variables

17. A t ratio which is calculated on data from a before-after design, using 20 subjects, should yield

*a. 19 degrees of freedom
   b. 38 degrees of freedom
   c. 18 degrees of freedom
   d. cannot tell from the above information

18. When a correlated t is applied to after-only data with independently assigned subjects then

   a. the positive correlation should be significant
*b. the correlation should equal zero
   c. the negative correlation should be significant
   d. the multiple R should be used

19. With any t test, correlated or independent, the final comparison is always drawn between measures of the

   a. independent variable
*b. dependent variable
   c. control variable
   d. none of these

20. Whenever Ho is accepted, when, in fact, it should have been rejected, the _____ error has been committed.

   a. alpha
*b. beta
   c. omega
   d. sampling

21. The more powerful a given statistical test is, the greater its likelihood of

*a. rejecting Ho
   b. accepting Ho
   c. detecting the alpha error
   d. reducing the degrees of freedom

22. Subtracting the beta error from the constant 1.00, yields

   a. the sampling error
   b. the deviation error
   c. bias
   *d. power

23. Whenever the value of the estimated standard error of difference is reduced,

   a. the value of the alpha error is increased
   b. the value of the sampling error is increased
   *c. the value of the t ratio is increased
   d. the value of the t ratio is reduced

24. The relationship between the size of the values for the estimated standard error of difference and the t ratio, is

   *a. inverse
   b. positive
   c. curvilinear
   d. impossible to determine

25. When the correlated t is used on data which are really independent, there is an increased likelihood of

   *a. accepting Ho
   b. rejecting Ho
   c. committing the alpha error
   d. none of these

26. When the independent t is used on data which are really correlated, there is an increased likelihood of

   a. rejecting Ho
   *b. accepting Ho
   c. committing alpha error
   d. none of these

27. The more powerful a given statistical test is, the more apt it is to

   *a. reject Ho when Ho should be rejected
   b. accept Ho when Ho should be rejected
   c. inflate the beta error
   d. trigger a statistical decision

28. Accepting the null hypothesis, when null should have been rejected causes the

   a. alpha error
   *b. beta error
   c. loss of degrees of freedom
   d. all of these, depending on the sample size

29. Rejecting the null hypothesis when it should have been accepted, causes the

   *a. alpha error   c. loss of degrees of freedom
   b. beta error   d. all of these, depending on the sample
                                         size

30. The probability of rejecting null always increases when the

    a. the alpha error is decreased
    b. sample size is decreased
    *c. sample size is increased
    d. power of the test is reduced

31. Compared to the independent t, the correlated t, on data which are
    really correlated, is

    a. a less powerful test
    *b. a more powerful test
    c. equal in power with the independent t
    d. none of these, since power is never a function of which statistical
        test is being used

32. When attempting to establish differences among three sets of matched
    interval scores, the appropriate test is the

    a. correlated t
    b. factorial ANOVA
    *c. within-subjects ANOVA
    d. multiple R

33. When the correlation between two sets of interval measures is
    significant, the value of the correlated t will <u>always</u> be

    *a. higher than the independent t
    b. lower than the independent t
    c. equal to the independent t
    d. none of these

34. In order to calculate a within-subjects ANOVA, one must first

    a. establish the value of the multiple R
    b. establish the values of the separate t tests
    c. establish the value of the Pearson r
    *d. none of these

35. When equating subjects on a matched-subjects design, the researcher
    should choose some measure which is correlated with the

    a. independent variable
    *b. dependent variable
    c. measurement scale
    d. confounding variable

36. Using a before-after design with a separate control group, helps to
    prevent

    a. sampling error
    b. score dispersion
    c. individual differences
    *d. confounding variables

37. Compared to the independent t, the correlated t for a given sample size
    <u>always</u>

    *a. has fewer degrees of freedom
    b. has more degrees of freedom
    c. uses degrees of freedom which are independent of the sample size
    d. none of these, since when sample sizes are fixed, so too are the
       degrees of freedom

38. When analyzing interval data from a before-after design, with a
    separate control group, the t ratio must be established between

    a. the "pre" and "post" scores
    b. the "post" scores, without reference to the "pre" scores
    c. the "pre" scores, without reference to the "post" scores
    *d. the "change" scores of the experimental and control groups

39. In a before-after design, with a separate control group the "change"
    scores must be

    a. correlated with each other
    *b. independent of each other
    c. positive in sign
    d. none of these

40. The within-subjects ANOVA should <u>never</u> be used

    a. on interval data
    b. on a matched-group design
    c. when more than two groups have been equated
    *d. none of these

41. When the correlation is <u>not</u> significant, the major difference between
    the correlated and independent t ratios, is in the

    *a. degrees of freedom
    b. the value of the estimated standard error of difference
    c. the value of the estimated standard error of the mean
    d. the value of the mean difference

42. Dividing the mean difference by the estimated standard error of
    difference <u>always</u> yields the

    a. standard error of the mean
    b. standard error of estimate
    c. standard error of proportion
    *d. t ratio

43. When using the independent t on interval data from a one-group,
    before-after design, there is an increased likelihood of

    a. sampling error
    *b. beta error
    c. alpha error
    d. rejecting Ho

44. When a researcher manipulates two independent variables simultaneously, the appropriate analysis must always utilize the

   a. independent t
   b. correlated t
   c. the one-way ANOVA
   *d. none of these

45. Regardless of the size of the sample, or the scale of measurement, when correlated samples are involved, the researcher may never use

   a. the correlated t
   b. the within-subjects ANOVA
   c. the appropriate degrees of freedom
   *d. none of these

46. When the probability of beta error increases, then

   a. so, too, does alpha error
   b. so, too, does sampling error
   c. so, too, does the power of the test
   *d. power decreases

47. When the calculated value of a correlated t, for a given number of degrees of freedom, equals the critical, table value of t, then

   a. Ho is accepted
   *b. Ho is rejected
   c. no statistical decision can be made
   d. the alpha error is reduced

48. With the within-subjects ANOVA, when null is rejected at an alpha of .05, then

   a. the alpha becomes .10
   b. the alpha becomes .01
   c. the alpha becomes .95
   *d. none of these

49. With any t test, independent or correlated, the loss of degrees of freedom causes

   a. an increased likelihood of rejecting Ho
   *b. a decreased likelihood of rejecting Ho
   c. an increase in the standard error of difference
   d. the mean difference to assume a negative value

50. For the t ratio, the only time a negative t value may occur is when

   *a. sample mean 1 is smaller than sample mean 2
   b. sample mean 2 is smaller than sample mean 1
   c. the sample means are equal
   d. none of these, since t may never be negative

51. For the t test, other things being equal, the smaller the estimated standard error of difference, the greater the likelihood of

   a. committing the beta error   *c. rejecting Ho
   b. accepting Ho   d. eliminating the test's power

52. Accepting Ho when it should have been accepted causes an increase in the

    a. alpha error
    b. beta error
    c. sampling error
  *d. none of these

53. With ratio data, calculating the t ratio is identical with the procedures used on

    a. nominal data
    b. ordinal data
  *c. interval data
    d. none of these, since with ratio data the t test cannot be used

54. With a within-subjects ANOVA, a significant difference implies that

    a. the difference occurs only in the sample
    b. the difference occurs in the population, but not in the sample
  *c. the difference occurs both in the sample and in the population
    d. there is no difference

55. For a given number of scores, the within-subjects ANOVA

    a. always has more degrees of freedom than does the independent F
    b. always has the same number of degrees of freedom as the independent F
  *c. always has fewer degrees of freedom than does the independent F
    d. has more degrees of freedom than the independent F when Ho is rejected

56. Sampling error is assumed

    a. only when the F ratio is calculated
    b. only when the t ratio is calculated
    c. only when the Pearson r is significant
  *d. whenever samples are measured

57. The only time the beta error may be committed is when the

    a. degrees of freedom are infinite
    b. degrees of freedom are less than 30
    c. degrees of freedom are calculated on the basis of sample size
  *d. none of these

B. True or False: For the following, indicate T (True) or (False)

53. The correlated t should not be used for the analysis   T
of data from independent sample groups.

59. For a given number of scores, the correlated t has one-half   T
the degrees of freedom of an independent t.

60. With an equal mean difference, when the correlation is   T
significant, the correlated t results in a higher t ratio
than does the independent t.

61. With a correlated t, a significant correlation has the effect   T
of reducing the value of the estimated standard error of
difference.

62. Degrees of freedom are a direct function of the sample size for all statistical tests except the correlated t.   F

63. When there is a correlation across the rows, the within-subjects ANOVA results in a higher value than when there is no correlation across the rows.   T

64. With interval data and a two, matched-subjects design, the appropriate analysis is via the independent t.   F

65. When analyzing data from a before-after design, if the correlation is not significant, the actual calculation of the independent and correlated t's becomes identical.   T

66. F may never be used on data from a matched-subjects design.   F

67. For a given mean difference, a significant correlation increases the value of a correlated t ratio.   T

68. The power of a test is equal to the summation of both the alpha and beta errors.   F

69. The lower the value of the beta error, the higher the power of any statistical test.   T

70. The beta error defines the probability of accepting null when, in fact, null should be rejected.   T

71. With an extremely powerful test, the probability of alpha error is eliminated.   F

72. With a correlated t, the greater the number of paired scores, the greater the number of degrees of freedom.   T

73. The use of the before-after design with a separate control group, prevents the possibility of manipulating the independent variable.   F

74. With interval data from a three-group, matched design, the appropriate test would be the within-subjects ANOVA.   T

75. Accepting Ho, when in fact Ho should have been accepted, results in the alpha error.   F

76. Other things being equal, the smaller the value of the estimated standard error of difference, the less likely the t ratio will be significant.   F

77. The correlated t may never result in a negative value.   F

78. The within-subjects ANOVA may never result in a negative value.   T

79. When analyzing interval data from a before-after design with a separate control group, an independent t may be applied to the two sets of "change" scores.   T

80. With 20 pairs of interval scores, the correlated t has 38 degrees of freedom.   F

81. The correlated t may only be applied to experimental   F
    data when there are at least two independent variables.

82. For the correlated t, increasing the sample size <u>always</u>   F
    increases the alpha error.

83. The higher the probability of accepting Ho, the greater   T
    the likelihood of committing the beta error.

84. For the correlated t, the fewer the degrees of freedom,   F
    the easier it becomes to reject the null hypothesis.

C. For the following questions, calculate the values. All correlated t's
   will be done via the long method, where the correlation is first checked
   for significance. Using the direct-difference method, because of
   rounding differences, may yield slightly different answers.

85. Calculate a correlated t on the following scores:

    Group 1   Group 2

       8   6
       7   6
       4   4
       <u>3</u>   <u>2</u>

    Ans.   2.44

86. For question 85, should Ho be rejected or accepted as a two-tail t?
    If accepted, state the alpha error.

    Ans. Accept Ho. Not significant.

87. Using the data from question 85, calculate an independent t.

    Ans.   .65

88. For question 87, should Ho be rejected or accepted as a two-tail t?
    If accepted, state the alpha error.

    Ans. Accept Ho. Not significant.

89. Calculate a correlated t on the following scores:

    Group 1   Group 2

      10   6
       4   4
      12   9
       5   3
       4   3
       6   5
       8   7
       <u>7</u>   <u>4</u>

    Ans.   4.35

90. For question 89, should Ho be rejected or accepted as a two-tail t? If rejected, state the alpha error.

Ans. Reject Ho. Significant at P < .01.

91. Using the data from question 89, calculate an independent t.

Ans. 1.54

92. For question 91, should Ho be rejected or accepted as a two-tail t? If rejected, state the alpha error.

Ans. Accept Ho. Not significant.

93. Calculate a correlated t on the following scores:

Group 1	Group 2
13	21
10	19
6	15
1	13

Ans. -10.80

94. For question 93, should Ho be rejected or accepted as a one-tail t? If rejected, state the alpha error.

Ans. Reject Ho. Significant at P < .01.

95. Using the data from question 93, calculate an independent t.

Ans. 2.99

96. For question 95, should Ho be rejected or accepted as a one-tail t? If rejected, state the alpha error.

Ans. Reject Ho. Significant at P < .05.

97. Calculate a correlated t on the following scores:

Group 1	Group 2
15	22
12	21
8	17
3	15

Ans. -8.98

98. For question 97, should Ho be rejected or accepted as a one-tail t? If rejected, state the alpha error.

Ans. Reject Ho. Significant at P < .01.

99. Using the data from question 97, calculate an independent t.

Ans. 3.00

100. For question 99, should Ho be rejected or accepted? If rejected, state the alpha error?

Ans. Reject Ho. Significant at P <.05.

For questions 101 through 105, use the following:

A researcher predicts that training on the balance beam reduces reading errors among learning disabled youngsters. A random sample of 9 children was selected from the population of learning-disabled children from a large metropolitan school district. They were all given a reading test and their errors recorded. They were then trained on the balance beam for one year, and again their error scores on the reading test recorded. The data follow:

Subject #	Before	After
1	12	10
2	12	10
3	2	1
4	6	4
5	6	5
6	7	7
7	10	9
8	9	8
9	11	8

101. Calculate the appropriate statistical test.

Ans. Correlated t equals 5.14

102. As a one-tail test, should Ho be rejected or accepted? If rejected, state the alpha error.

Ans. Reject Ho. Significant at P <.01

103. Had the researcher made an error and calculated an independent t, what value would have been obtained?

Ans. .95

104. For question 103, should Ho be rejected or accepted as a one-tail, ... as a two-tail? If rejected, state the alpha error.

Ans. Accept Ho. Not significant as a one or two-tail t.

105. What is the major research error in the design on this experiment?

Ans. There should have been a separate control group, since error scores could have improved with age. The independent variable has been confounded.

106. Calculate a within-subjects ANOVA on the following matched-subjects data:

Group 1	Group 2	Group 3
1	2	3
3	4	5
5	6	7
7	8	9
10	10	11

Ans. 58.14

107. For question 106, should Ho be rejected or accepted? If rejected, state the alpha error.

Ans. Reject Ho. Significant at $P < .01$

108. Calculate a within-subjects ANOVA on the following matched-subjects data:

Group 1	Group 2	Group 3
6	3	5
2	5	4
1	7	3
5	3	6
4	4	6

Ans. .47

109. For question 109, should Ho be rejected or accepted? If rejected, state the alpha error.

Ans. Accept Ho. Not significant.

110. Calculate a within-subjects ANOVA on the following matched-subjects data:

Group 1	Group 2	Group 3
1	5	6
3	4	7
5	3	8
4	6	10
2	2	4

Ans. 12.98

111. For question 110, should Ho be rejected or accepted? If rejected, state the alpha error.

Ans. Reject Ho. Significant at $P < .01$

112. Calculate a within-subjects ANOVA on the following matched-subjects data:

Group 1	Group 2	Group 3
1	2	3
3	3	6
5	6	11
4	5	9
2	4	6

Ans. 23.55

113. For question 112, should Ho be rejected or accepted? If rejected, state the alpha error.

Ans. Reject Ho. Significant at P < .01

For questions 114 through 116, use the following:

A researcher suspects that increasing illumination increases motoric speed. A group of 7 subjects was randomly selected and tested on the Digit Symbol subtest of the WAIS IQ test. The same subjects were tested under three illumination conditions, low light, medium light and high light. Their scores under each condition were as follows:

Subject #	Low Light	Medium Light	High Light
1	7	10	11
2	8	7	10
3	6	8	10
4	5	6	9
5	4	4	7
6	3	5	6
7	8	10	13

114. Calculate the appropriate F ratio.

Ans. 36.37

115. For question 114, should Ho be rejected or accepted? If rejected, state the alpha error.

Ans. Reject Ho. Significant at P < .01

116. What is the major research error in this study?

Ans. The practice effect was not controlled. Subjects may have improved their Digit Symbol scores simply by repeatedly taking the test. The independent variable was confounded.

117. A researcher sets up a before-after design with an independent control group. Calculate the appropriate t ratio.

EXPERIMENTAL GROUP		CONTROL GROUP	
Pre	Post	Pre	Post
100	109	100	106
98	110	110	115
106	113	95	102
108	116	105	111
110	116	102	107

Ans. Indpendent t on the "change" scores equals 2.36

118. Should Ho be rejected or accepted as a two-tail test? If rejected, state the alpha error.

Ans. Reject Ho. Significant at P < .05

119. A researcher sets up a before-after design with an independent control group. Calculate the appropriate t ratio.

EXPERIMENTAL GROUP		CONTROL GROUP	
Pre	Post	Pre	Post
10	20	8	16
6	14	12	16
11	20	6	12
8	18	9	12
5	12	8	10

Ans. Independent t on the "change" scores equals 3.41.

120. Should Ho be rejected or accepted as a one-tail test? If rejected, state the alpha error.

Ans. Reject Ho. Significant at $P < .01$

121. A researcher sets up a before-after design with a matched control group. Calculate the appropriate t ratio.

EXPERIMENTAL GROUP		CONTROL GROUP	
Pre	Post	Pre	Post
10	17	10	20
11	17	10	15
12	16	8	12
10	15	9	14
11	15	13	15
10	14	11	13

Ans. Correlated t on the "change" scores equals .43.

122. Should Ho be rejected or accepted as a one-tail test? If rejected, state the alpha error.

Ans. Accept Ho. Not significant as a one-tail or two tail.

For questions 123 through 125, use the following:

A researcher devises a special training program for high school students in order to increase their SAT scores. A random sample of 11 high school juniors is selected. They all take the SAT and their verbal scores are recorded. They then are given a three-month summer training program, entitled "Attacking the SAT". During November of their senior year they again take the SAT. Their verbal scores follow:

Junior Year Scores	Senior Year Scores
Pre	Post
504	520
500	526
550	575
550	574
550	573
480	503
450	471
300	319
600	617
400	416

Before publishing these data on the remarkable improvement resulting
from the summer program, the researcher is advised to use a separate
control group. Thus, another group of 11 students is selected who
did not attend the summer program, and matched to the first group
on the basis of IQ. Their junior year SAT scores were checked and
then compared with those received during November of their senior year.
The data follow:

Junior Year Scores	Senior Year Scores
Pre	Post
515	540
540	568
560	587
540	566
490	515
450	473
300	321
600	619
650	666
400	419
505	523

123. Calculate the appropriate t ratio.

Ans. Correlated t on "change" scores equals -4.14

124. Should Ho be rejected or accepted as a two-tail test?
If rejected, state the alpha error.

Ans. Reject Ho. Significant at $P < .01$

125. Which group did the results favor?

Ans. The group not attending the course.

CHAPTER 16
NONPARAMETRICS REVISITED: THE ORDINAL CASE

A. Multiple Choice Items

1. With the ordinal data, the important information being provided concerns

     a. equality versus non-equality
    *b. greater-than, or less-than
     c. the distance between the successive scale points
     d. an absolute zero

2. The most appropriate measure of central tendency on ordinal data is the

     a. mean
    *b. median
     c. mode
     d. interquartile range

3. Ordinal tests of significance are all

     a. parametrics
     b. non-parametrics
     c. distribution free
    *d. both b and c, but not a

4. Of the following correlation coefficients, which requires ordinal data?

     a. the Pearson r
     b. the coefficient of contingency
    *c. the Spearman r_s
     d. all of these

5. When the conversion is appropriate, it is always possible to convert

     a. nominal into interval data
     b. ordinal into interval data
     c. nominal into ordinal data
    *d. interval into ordinal data

6. In terms of the amount of information being contained in the measures, the following measurement scales rank

     a. first nominal, then ordinal, and then interval
     b. first ordinal, then nominal, and then interval
     c. first interval, then nominal, and then ordinal
    *d. first interval, then ordinal, and then nominal

7. In order to calculate an ordinal test of significance, the following must be true

     a. the scores must be normally distributed in the population
     b. the variability within each sample must be homogeneous
     c. the population means must be assumed to be equal
    *d. none of these

8. The X_r^2 (ANOVA by ranks) was created by

    a. Wilcoxon
    b. Mann and Whitney
    c. Kruskal and Wallis
 *d. Friedman

9. The T for correlated samples was created by

 *a. Wilcoxon
    b. Mann and Whitney
    c. Kruskal and Wallis
    d. Friedman

10. The U test was created by

    a. Wilcoxon
 *b. Mann and Whitney
    c. Kruskal and Wallis
    d. Friedman

11. The H test was created by

    a. Wilcoxon
    b. Mann and Whitney
 *c. Kruskal and Wallis
    d. Friedman

12. The ordinal test for assessing the difference between two correlated samples is the

 *a. T
    b. U
    c. H
    d. X_r2

13. The ordinal test for assessing the difference between three or more independent samples, is the

    a. T
    b. U
 *c. H
    d. X_r2

14. The ordinal test for assessing the difference between two independent samples, is the

    a. T
 *b. U
    c. H
    d. X_r^2

15. The ordinal test for assessing the difference among three or more correlated samples, is the

    a. T
    b. U
    c. H
 *d. X_r^2

16. The T test is the ordinal equivalent of which interval test?

    a.   independent t
    *b. correlated t
    c.   independent F
    d.   within-subjects ANOVA

17. The U test is the ordinal equivalent of which interval test?

    *a. independent t
    b.   correlated t
    c.   independent F
    d.   within-subjects ANOVA

18. The H test is the ordinal equivalent of which interval test?

    a.   independent t
    b.   correlated t
    *c. independent F
    d.   within-subjects ANOVA

19. The X_r^2 is the ordinal equivalent of which interval test?

    a.   independent t
    b.   correlated t
    c.   independent F
    *d. within-subjects ANOVA

20. The Pearson r is to the Spearman r_s, as the

    a.   F is to t
    b.   chi square is to V
    c.   H is to U
    *d. independent F is to H

21. When doing the ordinal T test, it is important to establish

    *a. the signed ranks
    b.   frequency of occurrence
    c.   the difference between the means
    d.   all of these

22. The ordinal T test shown in the text requires at least

    a.   12 pairs of scores
    b.   16 independent scores
    *c. 6 pairs of scores
    d.   25 independent scores

23. For the ordinal T on small samples, with a calculated value of 4.13 and a critical, tabled value of 6.00, then

    *a. Ho is rejected
    b.   Ho is accepted
    c.   Ho cannot be tested
    d.   the sample mean equals the parameter mean

24. For the ordinal T on small samples, with an obtained value of 17, and a critical, tabled value of 6.00, then

   a. Ho is rejected
   *b. Ho is accepted
   c. Ho cannot be tested
   d. the sample mean equals the parameter mean

25. Homogeneous variability within the various sample groups is required in order to calculate the

   a. U test
   b. H test
   c. Spearman r_s
   *d. none of these

26. Homoscedasticity is required in order to calculate the

   a. U test
   b. H test
   c. T test
   *d. none of these

27. If ordinal data are obtained from a two-group, after-only design (with random assignment of all subjects), the appropriate test would be

   *a. U
   b. T
   c. Spearman r_s
   d. X_r^2

28. If ordinal data were obtained from a three-group, matched-subjects design, then the appropriate test would be the

   a. T
   b. H
   c. U
   *d. X_r^2

29. If ordinal data were obtained from a one-group, repeated-measure design, then the appropriate test would be the

   *a. T
   b. H
   c. U
   d. chi square

30. If ordinal data were obtained from a four-group, after-only design, then the appropriate test would be the

   a. T
   *b. H
   c. U
   d. X_r^2

31. The Spearman r_s may only be used to test the hypothesis of

    a. difference
    *b. association
    c. equivalence
    d. none of these

32. Ordinal tests may be used to test data from the

    a. experimental method
    b. post-facto method
    *c. both of these
    d. neither of these

33. If the calculated value of z_u were 3.15 and the critical, tabled value were 1.96, then Ho would be

    *a. rejected
    b. accepted
    c. untestable
    d. none of these

34. Of the ordinal tests presented in the text, the only one which demands a reject of Ho when the obtained value is smaller than the critical, tabled value, is the

    *a. T
    b. Spearman r_s
    c. U
    d. none of these

35. Establishing whether the difference between two independently selected sample means is significant, requires the

    a. U test
    b. H test
    c. T test
    *d. none of these

36. Compared to the parametric tests, the non-parametrics have

    a. more assumptions
    *b. fewer assumptions
    c. the same number of assumptions
    d. all of these, depending on the scale of measurement

37. All non-parametric tests demand

    a. nominal data
    b. ordinal data
    c. interval data
    *d. none of these

38. When the assumptions of the interval tests are <u>not</u> met, the researcher should use

    a. parametric tests
    *b. non-parametric tests
    c. tests of association
    d. none of these

39. Compared to the Pearson r, the r_s is a

    a. more powerful test
*b. less powerful test
    c. test of equal power
    d. none of these, since power cannot be established for the r_s

40. The ordinal test, cited in the text, for testing the hypothesis of association is the

    a. Pearson r
    b. H
    c. T
*d. Spearman r_s

41. Regardless of the scale of measurement, the researcher analyzing data from a three-group, after-only design, must use the

    a. T
    b. U
    c. H
*d. none of these

42. Using a non-parametric test, when a parametric test **should** have been used, tends to

*a. reduce the likelihood of rejecting Ho
    b. increase the likelihood of rejecting Ho
    c. over-estimate the difference between the sample mean and the parameter mean
    d. none of these

43. If a Spearman r_s were used on data requiring a Pearson r, then in order to obtain significance

*a. a larger sample would be required
    b. a smaller sample would suffice
    c. the means of the two samples would have to deviate significantly from each other
    d. the population mean must be a known value

44. For a given sample size, the more powerful a test is, the more it is likely to produce

*a. significance
    b. a lack of significance
    c. a larger beta error
    d. none of these

45. The assumption of a normal distribution within the underlying population of scores, is required with the

    a. Spearman r_s
    b. U test
    c. chi square
*d. none of these

46. The hypothesis of difference may be tested by using

    a. the U test
    b. the H test
    c. the X_r^2
 *d. all of these

47. In order to test experimental data via the U test, the design must be

 *a. after-only
    b. before-after
    c. matched-subjects
    d. none of these, since U may not test experimental data

48. In order to test experimental data via the H test, the design must be

 *a. after-only
    b. before-after
    c. matched-subjects
    d. both b and c, but not a

49. Of the following, which may be used for the **analysis** of post-facto data?

    a. Spearman r_s
    b. H
    c. U
 *d. all of these

50. In order to test experimental data via the ordinal T test, the design must be

    a. after-only with independent assignment of subjects
    b. before-after
    c. matched-subjects
 *d. both b and c, but not a

51. In order to test experimental data via the X_r^2 (ANOVA by ranks), the design must be

    a. after-only with independent assignment of subjects
    b. before-after
    c. matched-subjects
 *d. both b and c, but not a

52. Whenever there is an increased probability of accepting null when null should have been rejected, then

    a. the beta error is increased
    b. the power is decreased
    c. there is a decreased likilihood of obtaining significance
 *d. all of these

53. The more powerful a given statistical test is, the more likely it is to produce

    a. beta error
    b. significance
 *c. non-chance results
    d. both b and c, but not a

54. Of the following, which does not belong with the others?

    a. U test
    b. H test
  *c. Pearson r
    d. T test

55. Of the following, which does not belong with the others?

    a. Pearson r
    b. Spearman r_s
    c. Coefficient of contingency
  *d. U test

56. Whenever non-parametrics are used instead of parametrics, then

    a. power is increased
  *b. power is reduced
    c. power is eliminated
    d. power becomes equal to .95

57. Under which of the following conditions does an increase in beta error lead to an increase in power?

    a. after-only design with ordinal data
    b. before-after design with interval data
    c. matched-subjects design with nominal data
  *d. none of these, since the premise is false

58. Of the following, which test has the least power?

    a. independent t
    b. correlated F
    c. correlated t
  *d. U test

B. True of False: For the following, indicate T (True) or F (False)

59. All parametric tests are less powerful than the   F
non-parametric.

60. Conditions which tend to increase the beta error,   F
also increase power.

61. Since it has so few assumptions, chi square may always be   F
used on ordinal data.

62. Ordinal tests require more assumptions than nominal tests.   T

63. Interval data may always be converted into ordinal data.   T

64. Ordinal data may always be converted into interval data.   F

65. All non-parametric tests are also distribution-free.   T

66. The concept of "greater than" or "less than" is at the   T
heart of the ordinal case.

67. The more power a test has, the more likely it is to produce significant results.   T

68. If a distribution of interval scores is badly skewed, the scores should be ranked and ordinal tests performed.   T

69. Ordinal data may never be skewed.   T

70. For a given sample size, the Spearman r_s is more powerful than the Pearson r.   F

71. The Friedman ANOVA by ranks does for ordinal data what the U test does for interval data.   F

72. The Spearman r_s does for ordinal data what the Pearson r does for interval data.   T

73. The U test makes no assumptions regarding the population parameters.   T

74. Beta error may only occur when the null hypothesis is accepted.   T

75. Non-parametric tests may never be used on data from post-facto research.   F

76. Beta error is the probability of being wrong whenever the null hypothesis is rejected.   F

77. The ordinal T for small samples only rejects null when the obtained value is equal to or less then the tabled value.   T

78. One cannot use the Spearman r_s on skewed interval data, unless the data has been converted into ordinal form.   T

C. For the following questions, calculate the values.

79. For the following distribution of interval scores, indicate, in order, the correct rankings. 110,55, 55, 50, 42, 42, 42, 30, 27.

    Ans. 1, 2.5, 2.5, 4, 6, 6, 6, 8, 9.

80. For the following distribution of interval scores, indicate, in order, the correct rankings. 799, 522, 515, 515, 515, 515, 515, 500.

    Ans. 1, 2, 5, 5, 5, 5, 5, 8.

For questions 81 through 86, use the following:

A researcher used a one-group, repeated-measure design, and established the following data:

Subject #	Scores Ranked by Rows		
	Measure 1	Measure 2	Measure 3
1	1	2	3
2	1	2	3
3	2	1	3
4	2	1	3
5	3	2	1

DATA CONTINUES ON NEXT PAGE

Subject #	Measure 1	Measure 2	Measure 3
6	1	2	3
7	1	2	3
8	3	1	2
9	1	2	3
10	2	3	1

81. Which statistical test should be used?

Ans. Friedman ANOVA by ranks

82. Calculate the appropriate statistical value.

Ans. $X_r^2 = 3.80$

83. Indicate the number of degrees of freedom.

Ans. 2

84. Indicate the tabled value at the .05 level.

Ans. 5.99

85. Indicate the tabled value at the .01 level.

Ans. 9.21

86. Should Ho be rejected or accepted. If Ho is rejected, state the alpha error.

Ans. Accept Ho. Not significant.

For questions 87 through 90, use the following

A researcher uses a three, matched-subjects experimental design, and establishes the following data:

Scores Ranked by Rows

Group 1	Group 2	Group 3
1	2	3
1	2	3
1	2	3
1	2	3
1	3	2
1	2	3
1	3	2
1	2	3
1	3	2
1	2	3

87. Which statistical test should be used?

Ans. Friedman ANOVA by ranks

88. Calculate the appropriate statistical value.

Ans. $X_r^2 = 15.80$

89. Indicate the number of degrees of freedom.

Ans. 2

90. Should Ho be rejected or accepted? If rejected, state the alpha error.

Ans. Reject Ho. Significant at P <.01

For questions 91 through 95, use the following:

A researcher sets up a one-group, before-after experimental design. Because the original, interval measures were badly skewed the data were converted into ordinal form.

Subject #	Pre-Rank	Post-Rank
1	1	1
2	3	2
3	2	7
4	5	3
5	7	4
6	6	8
7	8	9
8	10	5
9	9	6
10	4	10

91. Which statistical test should be used?

Ans. Wilcoxon T

92. Calculate the appropriate statistical value.

Ans. T=21.50

93. Indicate the critical, tabled value of T at .05.

Ans. 6

94. Indicate the critical, tabled value of T at .01.

Ans. 2

95. Should Ho be rejected or accepted? If rejected, state the alpha error.

Ans. Accept Ho. Not significant.

For questions 96 through 100, use the following:

A researcher sets up a two, matched-subjects experimental design, and collects ordinal measures on the subjects. The data follow:

Group 1	Group 2
1	4
2	5
3	6
7	8
9	11
10	12
13	13
8	7
11	9
12	10
4	3
5	2
6	1

96. Which statistical test should be used?

Ans. Wilcoxon T

97. Calculate the appropriate statistical value.

Ans. T = 36.50

98. Indicate the critical, tabled value of T at .05.

Ans. 14

99. Indicate the critical, tabled value of T at .01.

Ans. 7

100. Should Ho be rejected or accepted? If rejected, state the alpha error.

Ans. Accept Ho. Not significant.

For questions 101 through 105, use the following:

A researcher sets up a three-group, after-only design with random assignment of all subjects. Because the interval measures on the dependent variable are badly skewed, the measures are rank-ordered. The data follow:

Group 1	Group 2	Group 3
1	3	5
2	4	9
6	8	13
7	12	16
10	14	17
11	15	18

101. Which statistical test should be used?

Ans. Kruskal-Wallis H

102. Calculate the appropriate statistical value.

Ans. H = 13.59

103. Indicate the critical, tabled value at .05.

Ans. 5.99

104. Indicate the critical, tabled value at .01.

Ans. 9.21

105. Should Ho be rejected or accepted? If rejected, state the alpha error.

Ans. Reject Ho. Significant at P <.01.

For questions 106 through 108, use the following:

A researcher sets up a three-group, after-only design with random assignments of all subjects. All measures were originally taken in ordinal form. The data follow:

Group 1	Group 2	Group 3
1	3	5
2	4	6
7	9	11
8	10	12
13	14	15
16	18	17

106. Which statistical test should be used?

Ans. Kruskal-Wallis H

107. Calculate the appropriate statistical value.

Ans. H = 9.19

108. Should Ho be rejected or accepted? If rejected, state the alpha error.

Ans. Reject Ho. Significant at P .05

For questions 109 through 112, use the following:

A researcher wishes to find out if a speed-reading course increases reading speed. Sixteen subjects were randomly selected from the adult population and then randomly divided into two groups. Group A was given a speed-reading course, and then, because the interval scores were badly skewed, each subject was ranked according to reading speed. Their ranks were 1, 3, 4, 6, 8, 9, 10, 15. Group B received no training, and their ranks on the same test were 2, 5, 7, 11, 12, 13, 14, 16.

109. Identify the type of research.

Ans. Experimental, after-only

110. Which statistical test should be used?

Ans. Mann-Whitney U test

111. Calculate the appropriate statistical value.

Ans. 1.26

112. Should Ho be rejected or accepted? If rejected, state the alpha error.

Ans. Accept Ho. Not significant

For questions 113 through 116, use the following:

A researcher believes that athletic skill in basketball is a function of "handedness". A random sample of 24 professional basketball players was selected from the N.B.A., and divided into two groups according to preferred hand for shooting foul shots. The players were then ranked according to ability by a panel of sports writers. The data follow:

Prefer Right Hand		Prefer Left Hand	
	4		1
	5		2
	7		3
	10		6
	11		8
	13		9
n=13	14	n=11	12
	17		15
	18		16
	19		21
	20		22
	23		
	24		

113. Identify the type of research.

Ans. Post-facto, since handedness was assigned, not manipulated.

114. Which statistical test should be used?

Ans. Mann-Whitney U

115. Calculate the appropriate statistical value.

Ans. 2.44

116. Should Ho be rejected or accepted? If rejected, state the alpha error.

Ans. Reject Ho. Significant at P < .05

ANSWERS TO EVEN-NUMBERED TEXT PROBLEMS

CHAPTER 1

2. The ad is misleading, since we are not given the yearly production figures. Perhaps 90% of the cars built during the past 15 years, were, in fact, built only last year.

4. No. We must first examine the company profits of a year ago. An increase of 150% may, in fact, still be only a matter of pennies. Suppose that last year the company had earned 2 cents. The 150% increase would now only amount to 3 cents.

6. Nominal

8. Nominal

10. At least interval

CHAPTER 2

2. $\overline{X}$ = 39.50
   Mdn = 40.00
   Mo = 40

4. a. $\overline{X}$ = 63.22, Mdn = 63.00, Mo = 65 and 62
   b. The modes, since distribution is bimodal

6. a. $\overline{X}$
   b. Mo

8. To the right (Sk+)

10. Median

12. Mode, report both modes since the distribution is bimodal

14. T

16. F (To prove this, look at the set of scores in problem 3. Halfway between 3, the lowest score, and 100, the highest score, is 51.5. Yet the median is only 12.00)

18. F

20. F

CHAPTER 3

2. $\overline{X}$ = 10.38, R = 19, Standard Deviation = 7.26

4. a. R = 135 - 105 = 30
    b. Mdn = 118
    c. 122-114 = 8
    d. 129-107 = 22

6. A negative standard deviation should never be calculated

8. a. Leptokurtic
    b. Mesokurtic
    c. Platykurtic

10. At least interval

12. The variance has an approximate value of 15^2 = 225

14. F

16. F (it includes the middle 50%)

18. F (it includes the middle 80%)

20. T

CHAPTER 4

2. a. 91.77%
    b. 55.17%
    c. 19.49%
    d. 2.50%

4. a. 49.53%
    b. 94.43%
    c. 37.63%
    d. 22.17%

6. a. 99.87%, or percentile rank of 100
    b. .62%, or percentile rank of 1
    c. 56.75%, or percentile rank of 57
    d. 99.38%, or percentile rank of 99

8. a. 50   b. 50   c. 50

10. a. 50   b. 68   c. 95

12. F

14. T

16. T

18. T

20. T

2. a. 338.64
    b. 593.55
    c. 306.45
    d. 438.69

4. SD = 11.48

6. $\overline{X}$ = 33.38

8. a. 55.60
    b. 34.70
    c. 63.90
    d. 48.60

10. a. z's of -1.00 and +1.00
    b. T's of 40 and 60

12. T

14. T

CHAPTER 6

2. P = .65

4. a. P = .01
    b. P = .31
    c. P = .41

6. z's of =1.04 and +1.04

8. a. 24.34 and 26.90
    b. 23.20 and 28.04
    c. 19.98 and 31.26
    d. 12.45 and 38.79

10. a. P = .13
    b. P = .63
    c. P = .50
    d. 136.03 and 173.97
    e. 131.88 and 178.12

12. P = .01

14. P = 1.00

16. 50%

18. T

20. F

22. T

2. P = .16

4. a. .25
    b. z = -24.00 Reject Ho at P<.01

6. Population

8. Parameter

10. Sampling error

12. A sample mean

14. The standard error of the mean

16. 1. Random sampling from a single population
    2. Samples of sufficient size

18. F

20. F

22. T

24. Parameter

26. Parameter

28. Statistic

CHAPTER 8

2. t = 7.25 Reject Ho at both .05 and .01. The sample is probably <u>not</u> representative of a population whose mean is 60.

4. a. 33.38 to 36.62
    b. 32.84 to 37.16

6. a. 0.61
    b. 4.55 to 7.27
    c. 3.98 to 7.84

8. N-1 (sample size minus one)

10. Reject

12. Null must be rejected

14. .05

16. ± 1.96

18. Less likely   22. F

20. Increases   24. T

2. t = -1.59
    a. Accept Ho
    b. Yes (since Ho was not rejected)
    c. Since the two groups represent the same population of personality characteristics, no interpretation of "differences" is warranted.

4. 3

6. Zero

8. Less likely

10. Sampling distribution of differences

12. Alpha error (Type 1)

14. Null hypothesis (Ho)

16. F

18. F

20. F

CHAPTER 10

2. r = -.98
    Reject Ho, P<.01
    Taller children indeed have lower running times(run faster), but other factors, especially age and gender, should be considered.

4. r_s = .89
    Reject Ho, P< .01
    The correlation itself cannot determine the direction of the relationship. Perhaps better health produces income, or income produces better health care. Perhaps the mean with higher incomes were reared in upper socio-economic circumstances and received better health cara as children.

6. a. R_s = .14
    b. Accept Ho, correlation is not significant
    c. Although mixing starting pitchers with relievers may not be wise (since relievers often lose the opportunity for earning a "win"), it still appears that the general managers may not be overly prudent in their contract negotiations when only the previous season's performance is taken into consideration. It is possible that many of these high-salaried athletes have proven their value in past seasons and should not have to answer the question, "what have you done for me lately?

8. Because of the central tendency which typically occurs in both distributions.

10. Spearman r_s

12. Because the Pearson r is a more powerful test. It utilizes more information and is more likely to detect dignificance when there really is a correlation in the population.

14. T

16. T

18. T

20. F

CHAPTER 11

2. Hypothesis of difference: experimental

4. Hypothesis of difference: experimental

6. a. experimental (although because of the shifting audience, different
        subjects are used in the pre and post conditions.)
    b. before-after design
    c. Other variables which might confound are such things as: (1) weather
        (warm weather might increase Coke sales, and while buying Coke it
        might be easy to add popcorn), (2) the content of the movie, since
        scenes depicting eating behavior might induce hunger, (3) any change
        in the location or display of the Coke or popcorn booths could
        produce sales changes.

8. Whether or not the subjects received flouride; manipulated

10. Whether or not the subjects received coordination training; manipulated

12. The "subliminal" message; manipulated

14. Problem #4

16. Obtaining true matches on variables which are indeed known to be related
     to the dependent variable.

18. T

20. T

22. T

24. T

26. T

2. The HSD at .05 is 2.51, and at .01 is 3.32. All the differences which were significant occurred at .01.

	$\bar{X}_A$	$\bar{X}_B$	$\bar{X}_C$	$\bar{X}_D$	$\bar{X}_E$
$\bar{X}_A$	–	-2.33	-3.33 **	-4.67 **	-6.33 **
$\bar{X}_B$	2.33	–	-1.00	-2.34	-4.00 **
$\bar{X}_C$	3.33 **	1.00	–	-1.34	-3.00 *
$\bar{X}_D$	4.67 **	2.34	1.34	–	-1.66
$\bar{X}_E$	6.33 **	4.00 **	3.00 *	1.66	–

4. a. F = 19.33
   b. Reject Ho, P<.01
   c. The HSD at .05 is 4.30, and at .01 is 5.76

	$\bar{X}_A$	$\bar{X}_B$	$\bar{X}_C$
$\bar{X}_A$	–	-5.20 *	-10.00 **
$\bar{X}_B$	5.20 *	–	4.80 *
$\bar{X}_C$	10.00 **	4.80 *	–

6. F for rows (exercise) is 119.10, and is significant. Reject Ho, P < .01
   F for columns (temperature) is 41.71, and is significant. Reject Ho, P<.01'
   F for interaction is 2.45, and is not significant. Accept Ho.

   Whereas each of the main effects had a significant influence on the dependent variable, the interaction had no effect

8. The total mean

10. Larger

12. Between sum of squares and the Within sum of squares

14. Leptokurtic

16. Between

18. F

20. T

22. T

2. Chi Square = 6.00
   Reject Ho, P<.05
   The results differ significantly from chance

4. Chi Square = 4.46
   Accept Ho

6. Chi Square = 9.88
   Reject Ho, P <.01
   The results differ significantly from chance

8. Chi Square = .74
   Accept Ho; Difference not significant

10. Chi Square = 6.50 (with Yates)
    Reject Ho, P<.05
    Dorm students are more apt to get financial aid

12. Chi Square = 2.13
    Accept Ho (correlation not appropriate)

14. Nominal

16. Whenever an expected frequency is less than 10, and the df = 1

18. T

20. F

22. T

2. a. 85.70
    b. 103.70
    c. The prediction in part b is higher, since with a <u>lower</u> correlation
        the predicted Y value falls closer to the mean of the Y distribution.

4. 1988 - predicts earnings of $1.88
    1991 - predicts earnings of $2.33

6. a. 69.50
    b. 71.50
    c. 76.00

8. $R_{y.12} = .60$

10. a. 89.33 to 136.37
    b. 81.89 to 143.81

12. $R_{y1.2} = .38$

14. Regression line

16. Partial correlation

18. Mean of Y

20. a pair of scores

22. ± 1.00

24. T

26. T

28. T

30. T

2. $t = 2.74$
Reject Ho, $P < .05$

4. $t = 3.03$
Reject Ho, $P < .05$

6. $t = 4.45$
Reject Ho, $P < .01$
Attitude scores are significantly lower in the "after" condition.

8. It reduces it

10. It increases it

12. Reduces the likelihood

14. More able

16. F

18. F

20. T

22. T

24. T

CHAPTER 16

2. $H = 3.29$
Accept Ho

4. $X^2_r = 10.40$

    Reject Ho, $P < .01$

6. $X^2_r = 20$

    Reject Ho, $P < .01$
    Breathalyzer readings are reduced as time is increased

8. $z_u = 2.49$
Reject Ho, $P < .05$
Students significantly more verbally aggressive in small classes

10. Wilcoxon T

12. Kruskal-Wallis H

14. T

16. F

18. Mann-Whitney U

20. Friedman ANOVA by ranks